G000080077

THE RHINESTONE AS BIG AS THE RITZ

ALAN COREN

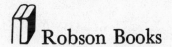

Robson Books

FIRST PUBLISHED IN GREAT BRITAIN IN 1979 BY
ROBSON BOOKS LTD., 28 POLAND STREET,
LONDON W1V 3DB. COPYRIGHT © 1979 ALAN
COREN

Coren, Alan
    The rhinestone as big as the Ritz.
    1. English wit and humour
    I. Title
    828'.9'1408   PN6175
ISBN 0-86051-056-5

All rights reserved. No part of this publication may be
reproduced, stored in a retrieval system, or transmitted in any
form or by any means, electronic, mechanical, photocopying,
recording or otherwise, without the prior permission in
writing of the publishers.

Printed and bound in Great Britain by Redwood Burn Limited,
Trowbridge & Esher

CONTENTS

Proem

My last collection, *The Lady From Stalingrad Mansions*, began, as millions of you will recall, with a prolegomenon.

Not surprisingly, I was inundated, after its publication, with sackfuls of complaints from readers angrily pointing out that they had had it up to here with prolegomena, you couldn't turn round these days without having them rammed down your throat, and reminding me that progress wasn't always all it was cracked up to be, when they were children there were green fields where now it's only tower blocks, supersonic jets, Bruce Forsyth, freeze-dried prawn curries, and, of course, prolegomena.

Why, they cried, use five syllables when only two would quite adequately serve? Was this not just one more example of proliferating bureaucracy, part of the gobbledegook of Watergate and VAT, the sort of thinking that sent all our driving licences to Swansea?

What was wrong, they continued, with a good old-fashioned proem? It had served their fathers, and their fathers before them, and had been part of the rich heritage of our language since, according to the OED, 1541, when you could take the whole family to Herne Bay, buy a slap-up eel dinner, get ringside seats for a cockfight, and still have change out of a groat.

I cannot but concur. A proem, after all, is just like a prolegomenon, really, only shorter.

. . . . .

Titler's Note:
By way of explanation: Scott Fitzgerald wrote a story called The Diamond As Big As The Ritz. The item in question belonged to Percy

Washington's father, and it made him the richest man in the world, which was what he wanted. I recounted this to my client, Mr Coren, one day at my office, and his lovely face crumpled in confusion. 'Why,' he enquired, 'would anyone want to have a diamond like that? If you had a rhinestone as big as the Ritz instead, it would impress your relatives just as much, and you wouldn't get mugged all the time.'

The Small Gatsby

'*Conservation, thrift, simplicity, self-containment, a withdrawal from conspicuous consumption and profligate competition, a rejection, indeed, of materialism—this seems to be the President's message. It is a considerable revision of the old American Dream.*'—U.S. News & World Report

IN MY YOUNGER and more vulnerable years my father gave me some advice that I've been turning over in my mind ever since.

'Whenever you feel like criticising anyone,' he told me, 'just remember that all the people in this world haven't had the disadvantages you've had.'

The reason I have been turning this over in my mind ever since is that it makes no goddammed sense to me at all. This may be because I had to leave school in the fourth grade on account of my parents ate my shoes. They had this thing about not eating animals due to where animals was running out, also not eating anything animals ate so that those animals who hadn't run out yet got to eat regular. In consequence, our family ate anything it could swallow, provided animals wouldn't touch it.

Since my father was one of the most influential paupers in our town, the streets was always full of fat animals and thin people. There was no cars. My father saw anyone driving past in an automobile and wasting precious fossil fuels with no thought to the welfare of his fellow man, he'd drag him right out from behind the wheel and kick him senseless.

When I was eighteen, I was sent East. This was because my father suspected I was developing a taste for potatoes which he calculated the world would run out of around 3150 AD; so that rather than run the risk of losing the family's good name for austerity and self-denial, they took me down to the station and shipped me to New York second-class freight. True, my mother had softened at the last and pushed into my crate through the air-hole a couple of tasty candles she had kept hidden from my father (who believed that world supplies of wax might not last the century), but beyond that and three dollars I had borrowed from the dog (the only one my father would trust not to buy gasoline when his back was turned), I had nothing in the world.

To cut a long story short, which you have to do these days due to where no novel is allowed to be more than four pages long on account of the trees are running out, I fetched up on Long Island Sound and took a nice hole on the beach at West Egg. West Egg is the somewhat less fashionable half of the Sound; you can look across the water to East Egg and see some very famous heads poking out of the sand—leading environmentalists thinking about the possibility of bio-degradable pebbles, leading conservationists working on schemes to harness flatulence, top international paupers with home-made teeth, famous society beachcombers in their seaweed skull-caps—but on the West Egg side there are still people on mains electricity who mix meat with their soya and who, if they don't go so far as actually to own an automobile themselves, certainly know people who own them.

Not that any of this was true of Gatsby.

Gatsby was the most deprived person my side of the Sound, and for all I know anywhere else, too. He had the hole next to mine, and it was just about the worst hole I ever saw. Most nights it fell on him.

Most nights, too, there was a party at Gatsby's hole. Gatsby threw the bleakest parties on the eastern seaboard. There was never anything to eat, and there was even less to drink; there wasn't any music, either, because even if Gatsby could have afforded a needle for a borrowed phonograph, the rigid ethics of the Sound would have prevented him from using it, on account of world supplies of iron was running out.

Everybody came to Gatsby's parties. People would walk from miles away, or if they were coming from East Egg, swim across the Sound: any night, you could see the gleaming lines of home-made flippers drawn up outside Gatsby's hole. But most of the guests never even met their host; they just came because it was a Gatsby party, but they never got around to asking who

10

Gatsby was or where he was, because they never got around to caring.

I used to wonder why Gatsby threw them. I don't think he liked them. He hardly ever went to them himself. I used to see him standing at the edge of the water in his formal pillow case, just staring out across the Sound towards East Egg.

Nobody ever knew how Gatsby had got to be so immensely poor. Some said he had started from very rich beginnings and managed, by investing ineptly, to ruin himself in less than a year. Some said he had started as a bootlegger on the day they repealed the Volstead Act. But it was generally agreed by the hard-faced bright-eyed brittle people who battened onto his hospitality that he had not been broke for very long: sons and daughters of old families who had been destitute for three generations sneered at their host for a *nouveau pauvre* while he stood motionless in the moonlight, gazing silently east.

The only people who never came to his parties that first summer were the Buchanans. Tom and Daisy Buchanan lived right across the Sound from Gatsby's place, in probably the most fashionable hole in all East Egg. Beautiful, idle, penniless, they were each of them descendants of great families who had been on relief since the early seventeenth century, a provenance unscarred by ownership, or waste, or despoliation, or success. Buchanans had been Nothing In The City for as long as anyone could remember, while Daisy's family had been the only people to travel steerage on the *Mayflower*.

Since Daisy was in fact a second cousin of mine, I had been settled in for less than a month when I paddled across to visit them. Their bright laughter tinkled like cut-glass, or broken old jelly-jars anyhow, when they saw my log, and I remember blushing and hoping against hope that they would put my ostentation down to boyish inexperience. I'm not sure that they ever did, since they lived their life on a plane beyond my understanding.

The very poor are different from you and me.

They were playing stick with a group of glittering young people as I walked up the beach. Stick was that year's elegant game, a form of polo played without horses, mallets, balls, goals, or jodhpurs. You found a stick and threw it about. It was really keen.

Daisy looked ravishing. From her earliest youth, she had avoided all soaps, shampoos, cosmetics, ornaments, anything, in short, that had come from animals or the earth and was likely to run out sometime, and it was on account of this that her lovely face selected itself from the company of its merely pretty peers like the beacon of its generation; which indeed it was. She put her grey cheek up for me to kiss, and when she laughed she exposed a row of fashionably neglected teeth lovely as datestones, and when she tossed her head in calculated nonchalance, her uneven ringlets slapped lankly against her pimple-peeping neck like cold tagliatelle.

'Nick!' she cried. 'Where have you been keeping yourself?'

'I'm over on West Egg,' I replied. 'I have a hole right next to Gatsby's.'

At Gatsby's name, I felt a ripple shiver the slim body in my arms, right through the gunny sack.

'Gatsby?' she murmured faintly.

'Surely you know him? He throws those fabulous . . .'

'Oh, she knows Gatsby all right!' cried Tom Buchanan suddenly. 'He used to come by here with his begging bowl after he moved in across the Sound. God knows who he was trying to impress with his poverty! I believe he once told Daisy his parents had starved to death. Do you know, Carroway, I think she actually believed him for a while?'

'That was a long time ago, Tom,' whispered Daisy.

'Yes!' shouted Buchanan, his eyes blazing in his grime-caked handsome face. 'And I made a few enquiries and discovered that far from having starved to death, his people actually owned the New Haven & Hartford Railroad and spent half the year on their diesel yacht in Monte Carlo!'

'Diesel!' I exclaimed. 'Europe! Poor Gatsby!'

'*Poor* Gatsby indeed!' thundered Buchanan. 'Rich, ambitious, greedy, wasteful Gatsby, more like! Rotten little parvenu!'

Daisy pulled away from me, and I could see she had been crying. There were deep grooves in her cheeks. I figured it best that I leave. But before straddling my log again, a thought occurred to me.

'He's throwing a party Saturday night,' I called. 'Why not come?'

12

Daisy nodded her lovely head, so that the encircling flies spun off in crazy pirouettes.

'We'll be there,' she said.

Gatsby could hardly contain himself. When I shouted the news into his hole, he started so violently that it took me best part of an hour to dig him out. It was then that I realised that Daisy Buchanan represented something to Jay Gatsby that I had not even begun to guess at. He took my arm in a rough grip and led me to the water's edge, and pointed out across the Sound.

'Useta be a green light on the end of her, you know, dock,' he muttered.

'Really?'

'No fooling, I swum over and stuck it there myself. So's I could look at where she was nights. It had this, like, eternacell battery, size of your finger, useta glow.' He turned hollow eyes to me. 'I mean, how much goddamn energy can a thing like that use?'

'I've never seen it,' I said.

'That's on account of where they found it, also kicked it in the goddamn sea right after,' he said. 'She sent me this note about what kind of bum uses up the precious resources of Planet Earth sticking green lights on people's premises. She continued only a parvenoo bum, that's what kind of bum. I never saw her again, old sport.'

'I see,' I said.

'Who'd have figured it?' he said quietly, to himself. 'All that godamn fuss about a green light? What is it with poor people, Nick?'

'I have to go and get dirty for your party,' I said.

I never saw him again.

There was a freak tide Safurday evening, and by the time I'd finished baling out my hole and got over to Gatsby's place, the party was over. There was just Gatsby under a sheet with this red stain on it, and a guy with home-made-spectacles staring at it. Or near it, anyhow. That's one of the troubles with home-made spectacles.

'Rich son-of-a-bitch,' he said.

'What happened?' I asked.

'Middle of the party, guy busts in, says his name is Wilson and when is Gatsby going to settle his garage bill. Everybody stops suddenly and looks at Gatsby. Daisy Buchanan says there has to be some mistake, Gatsby don't have no automobile. Wilson says for her to stop putting him on, if Gatsby don't have no automobile, what is that interesting green foreign job he drives into Wilson's garage every Friday and fills up with super? Gatsby suddenly screams that Wilson is lying, so Wilson pulls out this large iron item and blows Gatsby away.'

I looked down at the sheeted corpse.

'Someone ought to go see Daisy Buchanan,' I said.

'The Buchanans ain't there,' said the owl-eyed man. 'They shut their hole for the summer. Daisy says the wrong class of people is moving in, next thing it'll be TV and barbecued spare ribs. They went to stay with some people they know on the Bowery.'

Owl-eyes shambled off towards the water, and splashed away. I watched his ripples spread out towards Daisy's lightless dock. Gatsby had come a long way to this dark beach, and his dream must have seemed so close that he could hardly fail to grasp it. He did not know that it was already behind him, somewhere back in that vast obscurity beyond the city, where, one by one, the cars were grinding slowly to a halt.

Down Below

'A neolithic flint adze thrown up by excavators at Sinfin Moor, near Derby, is puzzling archaeologists. It was buried far deeper than is typical of the period.'—Daily Express

HE LIMPED WEARILY into the cave, and threw down his spear.

'Here!' she cried. 'I just done that step.'

'Step?' he snorted. 'Call that a *step*? Bloody rock stuck in the middle of the floor, that's what *that* is. It don't go up to nothing, and it don't go down to nothing. It's just there for bloody falling over on.'

She glared at him bitterly, the firelight empurpling her woad.

'It'd be a step,' she muttered, 'if we had a door. You could step on it and push through. Nice goatskin door, with a hole in it so you could keep an eye open for the next Ice Age. Something tasteful. Not flash.'

'Doors!' he cried. 'It'll be huts next.'

She lifted a dripping hoof from the pot, sniffed it, and let it fall back again into the bubbling scum.

'Why not?' she said.

'Because we're not bloody hut-dwellers, that's why not! Cave-dwellers is what we are, always have been, always will be. You know where you are with a cave, you got security, you got a mountain behind you. Nothing comes up on you sudden. I seen huts. Catch me kipping down in a hut, bloody mammoth come up in the night, great big feet, you'd wake up in the morning and find you was living on a raft. If,' he added darkly, 'you woke up at all.'

'There aren't any mammoths,' she said.

'They'll be back,' he said. 'Weather perks up a bit, you won't be able to move for bloody mammoths. There'll be hut-

15

dwellers smeared all over the place.'

'I don't see why that stops us hanging a door over the front of the cave,' she said. 'It's so primitive, everyone looking in, dogs widdling on the fire.'

'Never mind bloody primitive!' he shouted. 'Hang a door on, I wouldn't see nothing going past would I? Fat lot of use it is being a hunter, can't see stuff going past, you'd only hear it clatter, time you picked up your spear and got through the bloody goatskin, your dinner'd be a galloping bleeding dot, it'd be roots and berries seven days a week, not to mention status up the spout. Can't come home with a root slung over your shoulder, can't walk into a village with a bleeding loganberry on the end of your spear. I'd be a laughing stock.'

She sighed.

'I'd settle for a shelf,' she said.

'A what?'

'A shelf. It's a long flat piece of rock for putting things on. You fix it to the wall. It adds character to a home.'

'What things?' he said, furrowing his imperceptible brow. 'We haven't got any things. Few bones from last week, the odd skull, that's all. Various droppings. I shouldn't think you add much character to a home with a shelfload of skulls and droppings.'

'We'd get things,' she said. 'Interesting pebbles, stuff like that.'

He stared at her, a nit poised, uncrushed, between thumb and forefinger.

'*Interesting pebbles?*' he cried. 'What's bloody interesting about a pebble?'

She shrugged, spread her thin hairy hands, desperate.

'You can find ever such amusing shapes,' she said, finally.

His stare did not waver, though the nit popped softly.

'Ho yes, very droll,' he said. 'Come home after a hard day's hunting, cheesed off, trod on, wore out, gored, take a quick shufti at my shelf with its hilarious pebble collection and start rolling around on the floor, clutching my ribs, nicely set up for the evening! Yes, it takes you out of yourself, a nice comical pebble, that's what I always say.'

She turned her head away.

'There's *some* caves,' she murmured distantly, 'with pictures on the walls. I've heard. Men running after buffalo, men waving

16

at wolves. In colour.'

'It takes all sorts,' he said. 'You ought to have married one of them. Interior decorator, dandelion in his ear, poncing about with his paintpot, banging up goatskin drapes, mincing off after uproarious gravel. Standing there with his hand on his hip drawing buffalo, instead of going out after the buggers with a sharp stick in all weathers, come home drenched, arm bit off more than likely, and not a word of gratitude, only people going on and on about shelves.'

'*You've* never come home with buffalo,' she said. 'Our community's not seen nothing bigger than a dog for donkey's years, and not many of them. If we had pictures on the walls of *our* caves, they'd show men running after voles.'

'Give you a nasy nip, voles,' he retorted. 'Easy to see you've never cornered a vole with his rag up. *And* full of flavour.'

She gave the cauldron an absent stir.

''Course, it's a skilled job, making a shelf,' she said.

'*Skilled?* Finding a piece of rock, call that skilled? Vole leaping at you downwind, half a second to bring your javelin up or lose a bloody ear, *that's* skilled. People today, they take hunting for granted, no idea what goes into it, years of experience, eye like a hawk, nerves of, er . . .'

He fell, groping, into silence.

'It's not the finding,' she said, 'it's the making. It's got to be oblong, it's got to have . . .'

'What's oblong?'

'Like a wheel, but longer on two sides. You'd have to shape it.' She smoothed her voleskin shift. 'Bit beyond your average hunter, that.'

His mouth fell open, hung, and snapped shut again.

'RIGHT!' he roared.

And went out.

Two days later, on a bleak Peak upland, he found what he was looking for, and dragged it home. He laid it outside the cave, and brought her out to see it.

'It's three times as long as you are,' she said. 'We'd never find the stuff to fill that.'

'I haven't shaped it yet, have I?' he said.

And began to gnaw.

She watched for a while, vaguely stirred by a sense that all was not as it should be, and went inside again.

After an hour or so, he stopped, and spat out assorted fragments, most of them teeth. He stared at the unremitting slab.

'Stone me!' he muttered, not having developed a sense of humour. 'Start with furniture, where's it going to end? Mouthful of gum, and her bloody cooking, I could suck myself to death.'

He was still gazing wretchedly at the rock when four hunters loped past after the day's work.

'Here he is,' said the first.

'Bloody hell,' said the second, 'he's eating a rock!'

'He won't be the only one,' said the third, 'if this goes on.' He dropped to a crouch, bitterly. 'We could have done with you today, squire,' he said. 'Cornered this hedgehog, didn't we? Would've had him, too, if you'd been there to close the circle up. As it was, he give us the wossname, slip. Can't half scuttle, hedgehogs.'

'Where've you been?' enquired the third.

'I'm making this shelf, aren't I?' he replied.

They reeled.

'*Making a shelf?*' they shrieked.

'For the wife.'

'*For the wife?*'

Beneath the matted hair, a blush suffused his sloping cheeks.

'Werl, I'll be back hunting in a day or so,' he muttered, 'soon as it's up.'

'Not with us, you won't,' said the first hunter.

'Right,' said the second. 'You stay here, son, help round the cave. Keep an eye on the stew, know what I mean?'

'Knock up a pinny or two,' said the third, nudging the others, 'make yourself some slippers. Build a chair.'

'*Build a chair!*' shrieked the others, clutching their sides and falling against one another helplessly.

Whereupon, having recovered their breath, they sprinted off at a virile trot.

He stood up, shaking with rage, and was about to dash the slab to fragments when he noticed his wife's eyes gleaming at him from the cave-depths, challenging him to recognise defeat.

He sat down again, and recommenced his agonised nibbling.

It got him nowhere. He stopped. He racked as much brain as he could muster, glowering at the thing that refused to become a shelf. And then he picked up a chunk of flint and struck at it. A piece of rock flew off. He struck again, and another piece shot past his ear.

After an hour or so, a reasonable oblong lay upon his knees, and a victorious leer rippled his enormous underlip. He began to bevel the edge of the oblong with delicate, assured strokes, humming atonally the while, and so preoccupied that he did not hear the soft feet pad up behind him.

'What's this, then?' said a voice.

He glanced up. Three men in well-cut sheepskins were glaring down at him.

'I'm making a shelf,' he said, proudly.

The three men looked at one another.

'Making a shelf,' said the tallest of the three.

'There we are,' said the second. 'Soon as I heard the chipping, I knew. Someone's using a tool, I said, didn't I?'

That's what you said,' replied the third. 'Someone's using a tool.'

'Tool?' said the man with the shelf.

'Give it here!' snapped the leader, reaching out. He turned the flint in his calloused hands. 'Bloody stroll on,' he cried, 'he's only gone and got himself an adze!'

'It's an ordinary flint,' protested the shelfmaker.

'Pull this one!' cried the second. 'We know a bleeding adze when we see one. Skilled toolmakers like us, spend a lifetime chipping things, don't give us all that rubbish!'

'That's it then,' said the leader. 'Hunter found using an adze. I'll have the lads out from here to the bloody Wirral!'

'Taking bread out of people's mouths, brother!' cried the second, tapping the shelfmaker in the chest.

'Contrary to subsection fourteen!' shouted the third.

'Not to mention the alleged shelf,' said the leader. 'Not my area, of course, but I wouldn't like to be in your feet when the Amalgamated Builders get to hear about this.'

'Right!' said the second. 'Don't find us going out after buffalo, do you, brother? Bloody voles, day in, day out, but that don't mean we go off on our tod after buffalo, poaching on someone else's professional wossname.'

'You want a shelf, mate,' muttered the leader, putting his face up close, 'there's proper channels!'

And, drawing themselves up to almost their full height, the three toolmakers moved off at a brisk sidle.

He was still sitting there as the gloaming began to shade the hillside, and he did not look up as his wife materialised out of the dropping dark.

'You've stopped, then?' she said.

He cleared his throat.

'I've had it with the hunters,' he said quietly, 'and the Toolmakers have walked out, and in all likelihood the Amalgamated Builders are going to come round any minute and jump on my face.'

'What for?' she said.

'On account of my shelf,' he replied, turning it lovingly to what was left of the light.

She looked at it.

'Call that a shelf?' she said.

So he walked a little way down the hill, and he dug a very deep hole, and when it was finished he dropped the adze in, and he filled the hole up again with earth.

And walked back up the hill again, wondering if tomorrow mightn't be a good day for buffalo.

When You and I were Buddies on the Sidewalks of New York

'New York police, who pride themselves on being the world's toughest cops, will soon be recruiting homosexuals. New mayor Edward Koch marked his first day in office by drawing up a gay rights charter which makes it illegal to discriminate against them in hiring police and firemen.'—Daily Mail

AT 7.04 AM, a rim of winter sun touched the leafless trees in Central Park. By 7.12, it had edged the cold stone bridge with orange. By 7.16, it had begun to colour the body that lay on the bridge. The orange came from the sun. The red came from somewhere else.

It was a morning jogger who called the cops. When the black-and-white wailed up at 7.23, the jogger was leaning over the parapet of the bridge, retching. The two cops got out and looked at him.

'Oh my God!' muttered Patrolman Kowalski. 'He's going to *ruin* that tracksuit!'

They minced quickly across. Patrolman Vidal helped the jogger upright, gently.

'It's horrible,' said the jogger. He was middle-aged, paunchy, grey-faced. 'It's the most horrible thing I ever saw.'

'It's not so bad,' said Kowalski. 'I know this really terrific hand-laundry on the corner of Lexington and 44th, they can do miracles. All the guys go there. Cottons, man-mades, even silks, they can bring them right up like new. Am I right, Jerome?'

'Ask for Cheryl,' said Vidal to the jogger. 'He's very tall, kind of willowy, but with these big capable hands. I got muscatel on this kimono I had one time, I thought it would kill me, but Cheryl got right to work . . .'.

21

'I mean the corpse,' croaked the jogger. He pointed, waveringly.

'I know what you mean,' said Kowalski. 'A canary coat with damson pants, he looks like some kinda cheap dessert.'

'The back of his head,' said the jogger, 'it's shot away.'

'You haven't touched anything?' said Patrolman Vidal.

'Of course not.'

'Don't be offended,' said Kowalski. 'Some guys are very freaky for cadavers. We had a lieutenant in our precinct one time, he always came to station stag nights in white pancake and a shroud. I couldn't relate to him at all. Nor could Jerome.'

'He could tango like there was no tomorrow,' said Vidal, 'but his neck always smelled of formaldehyde. It was really, you know, weird. Like it was some kinda deliberate turn-off.'

'I think he was a closet straight,' said Kowalski, picking a strand of thread that had caught in Vidal's badge and was blowing in the keen morning wind. 'I heard he got married after he transferred to Yonkers.'

'Look, I don't want to put my, you know, where it's not wanted, but don't you think you ought to report this?' said the jogger.

'Oh my God,' sighed Vidal, 'it's rush-rush-day, everyone! Next thing you're gonna be telling us you're a taxpayer, right?'

He trotted delicately back to the patrol car, snatched up the dash-mike.

'Car 64, Patrolman Vidal here, we have a 286 in the park, possible . . . oh, hi, Bruce! I didn't recognise your voice, you're so *throaty* sometimes, did you manage to get bean sprouts? Oh, hey, that's really terrific, Maurice and I can pick up the lychees on the way back. What? Yeah, a dead one, took it in the head. Oh, come *on*, Bruce, lousy old jokes is the last thing I need this time in the morning! What? I don't know, I haven't turned him over, I'll ask Maurice.' He leaned back out of the car window. 'Hey, Maurice, what does he look like?'

'It's not too easy to say, with half a head and all,' called Kowalski, who was kneeling by the body, 'but he's kind of the Burt Reynolds type.'

'Jesus!' muttered Vidal. 'Maurice says he reminds him of Burt Reynolds, Bruce. Bruce? Oh my God, Brucie, don't do one of your weepie numbers on me, listen, the guy was wearing a canary jacket with purple pants, you'd have *hated* him. Also, he was wearing sneakers, a real schlock, even this straight jogger threw up. You wanna send Homicide over now? Great! What? Oh, come *on*, Brucie, not over the line, there could be people listening, anyway the park is filling up, there's folks all around. Sure I do, Bruce. No, really, I mean it. Ten four.'

At 7.58, a lilac convertible purred up to the bridge. Two detectives got out. Their cheeks were crimson with cold. Their ears glowed.

'You took your time,' said Kowalski, consulting the wafer-thin Patek Philippe fob-watch that hung, its tiny baguettes twinkling, just below his badge.

The lieutenant took a step forward, so that his jutted jaw was a millimetre from the patrolman's nose. He was half a head taller, and twice as wide in the shoulder. From these shoulders, his oblong head rose neckless, like a bristled rock.

'Where do you get off criticising *me*, you bitch!' he shrieked.

'Easy, Lewis,' murmured his sergeant, 'everyone's looking.'

The lieutenant glanced quickly around, flashed his gold bridgework, shot his jade cufflinks, tossed his bullet-head.

'We came via Harlem,' explained the sergeant to Kowalski. 'We had the top down, we thought we'd cruise a little, Lewis is very into blacks right now.'

'I like the new paint job,' said Kowalski.

The lieutenant, who had walked a little way off and, arms furiously folded, been tapping his crocodile-shod foot, now turned, mollified.

'Thank you, Maurice,' he said. He smiled. 'You don't think the leopardskin is maybe a little *outré*?'

'I think *you* can get away with it, sir,' said Kowalski. 'I mean, very, very few people could get away with it, but *you*, no problem.'

'Well, thank you, Maurice. Don't call me sir. You have really terrific taste, I've noticed that before. Hasn't Maurice got really terrific taste, Bernard?'

The sergeant stared smoulderingly at the lieutenant.

'I don't see where it's so goddam terrific,' he muttered. 'You wouldn't catch me dead in black barathea. I think you're getting to be a uniform freak in your old age, Lewis.'

'I didn't *choose* this lousy outfit, Bernard!' snapped Kowalski.

'It's my dream to go plain clothes. I have this marvellous imported cashmere poncho from Saks Fifth Avenue, I've been just dying to wear it to work, it has the terrific added advantage of where you can draw and fire from under it, not to mention where the holster doesn't ruin the line of your suit in the first place, it could be *very* big.'

'I think that's a wonderful idea, Maurice!' cried the lieutenant. 'We could *all* have them, it could sweep the entire NYPD, don't *you* think that's a wonderful idea, Bernard?'

'What *I* think,' said the sergeant, 'is that some of us might be just a *teeny* bit, well, bulky for it, mightn't we, Lewis?'

'I don't think Lewis is bulky at all,' cried Kowalski. 'He's big, yes, but he can carry it. He has the walk. I am reminded of Broderick Crawford.'

The lieutenant looked at him.

'I had no idea you wanted to go into the plain clothes squad, Maurice,' he said. 'You should have said.'

'I flunked my orals,' said Kowalski.

They looked at him for a while. A lark rose, busily, across the bridge.

The lieutenant cleared his throat.

'Anytime you want to become a detective, Maurice,' he said, 'you give me a call, okay?'

They were still smiling into one another's eyes when the jogger came up to them.

'Look,' he shouted, 'what are you gonna do about this goddam corpse, I am waiting to give a statement, I am freezing my butt off here, I ought to be taking a shower, your muscles can lock solid, I ought to be at Schlumkiss, Schlumkiss, Terwillikin & Schlumkiss, I am a taxpayer in this lousy . . .'

'Who,' murmured the lieutenant, 'is the little creep in the drecky ready-to-wear?'

'He found the body sir, I mean Lewis,' said Kowalski. 'I told him to take the tracksuit to Cheryl.'

'You did good, Maurice,' said the lieutenant. 'Personally, I would take it to the garbage chute, but *chacun à son moutons, n'est-ce pas?*'

'My God, you speak French!' cried Kowalski.

'*Un petit peu,*' said the lieutenant.

'That's wonderful,' said Kowalski, 'you wouldn't believe how embarrassed I get when Jerome tries to order sometimes. Do you know that truly marvellous new little Basque restaurant on 54th Street, they have a way of folding the escargots in a . . .'

'ARE YOU GOING TO TAKE A STATEMENT FROM ME OR ARE YOU NOT?' screamed the jogger.

'Oh, for goodness sake!' exclaimed the lieutenant, rolling his piggy eyes upwards. 'What is this life, if full of care etcetera, baby?'

'I guess you ought to take a look at the body, Lewis,' murmured Kowalski.

'Okay, Maurice, but just for you, I want to make that absolutely clear.' He glanced over the jogger's agitated head, towards the bridge. 'Oh, yeah, why looky here, it's a stiff!'

'Aren't you gonna go any closer?' shouted the jogger.

'What are you, crazy or something?' snapped the lieutenant. 'I have enough trouble sleeping nights without going right up to people, they have their lousy head shot away!'

'*You* have trouble sleeping?' enquired Kowalski. 'You look so, I don't know, *secure*. I'd never have guessed.'

'I had a bad week, Maurice,' said the lieutenant. 'We had this kid holed up in a liquor store, we had to rush him, I broke my heel.'

Kowalski was still commiserating when Patrolman Vidal came up. He glared at his colleague.

'Just in case you hadn't noticed, Maurice,' he muttered, 'this is one of my Looks!'

'I'm sorry to have left it all to you, Jerome,' said Kowalski, 'I was talking to the lieutenant.'

'I noticed.'

'Don't be that way, Jerome. It isn't like you. Did you find anything on the body?'

Vidal sniggered.

'I thought you'd never ask,' he said.

'I don't like you when you simper, Jerome,' said Kowalski. 'Did you identify the victim?'

Vidal shook his head.

'Nothing on him,' he said, 'except this locket.'

Kowalski took the little golden heart.

'Open it,' said Vidal.

'Oh my God!' cried Kowalski, staring.

'What is it, Maurice?' asked the lieutenant.

Kowalski caught his breath, held out the dangling locket.

'It's—it's a picture of you, Lewis,' he stammered.

The lieutenant gasped. He staggered. He clutched the lilac convertible for support. But he was a cop, and a good one. He bit his lip. He recovered. He removed his grey fedora.

'Take your hats off, boys,' he muttered. 'They shot the Commissioner.'

Publish and be Diblgd!

The Daily Telegraph *recently published a missing chapter, dropped by the author, from* Through The Looking-Glass. *Disappointing in itself, its real revelation was that Lewis Carroll was prepared to cut and change his work to meet objections by illustrators, publishers, printers, and almost anyone else. Which at last explains one of the greatest literary conundrums in the language . . .*

THE JUNIOR PORTER of Christ Church College, Oxford, came out of his cubby-hole and squinted across the cold cobbled acreage of Tom Quad. The Senior Porter was standing in the fountain, poking a twig up a spout. The Junior Porter trotted across on echoing clogs.

'Where is he this time?' he said.

The Senior Porter removed the twig. He examined the end through sweat-blobbed pince-nez.

'See that?' he said, 'Know what that is? Bleeding caviare, that's what that is. Bleeding sturgeon's eggs rammed up the outlet.'

'Stone me!' cried the Junior Porter. 'What is the eternal mystery of the sturgeon that it will swim thousands of miles upstream from bloody anywhere to lay its eggs?'

The Senior Porter removed the pince-nez, and stared at him.

'God Almighty, Scrimweasel,' he muttered. 'Could it be Mr Darwin was on the right track, after all? Is it true as how you are paid in bananas?'

'I don't follow,' said Scrimweasel, sullenly.

''Course you don't,' said the Senior Porter. He shook his head. 'The eternal mystery to what you are referring concerns the salmon, son. The sturgeon just bleeding lies there, as you'd expect, being a protected species. It just bleeding lies there in

27

the sea, and its eggs come out. They only get up brass bloody spouts as the result of japes on the part of your titled undergraduates, coming home on the outside of two gallons of claret, going "Haw! Haw! Haw!", and poking bloody caviare up brass conduits.'

'Oh,' said Scrimweasel.

'I bin here since 1831,' said the Senior Porter, 'during which time what I have took out of College drains, gullies, bogs, pipes, and students, is nobody's business. There is more to this job than posing for bloody Ackermann, sunshine.'

'Well, then,' countered Scrimweasel, 'if you're so smart, where is Mr Charles Lutwidge Dodgson, then?'

'Smirk at me, lad, I'll knock your 'ead off!' snapped the Senior Porter.

'Sorry,' muttered Scrimweasel. 'I got this note for him, haven't I?'

The Senior Porter consulted an enormous turnip watch. He looked, thought Scrimweasel privately, much like a white rabbit.

'Eleven a.m.,' said the Senior Porter. 'Boar's Hill Junior Girls'll be coming out for 'ockey. You'll find him up the tower with his telescope.'

'Bloody stroll on!' cried Scrimweasel. 'That's two 'undred steps!'

'Take your time,' said the Senior Porter. 'You don't want to come up on him sudden, know what I mean?'

The Junior Porter coughed, discreetly. But the wind snatched it away, so he coughed again, more sharply.

The Senior Lecturer in Mathematics jumped.

'Ha! Ha!' he shrieked. 'Scrimweasel! I was just, er, inspecting the Meadows. There is talk of a by-pass.'

' 'Course you were, squire,' said the Junior Porter. He held out the note. Dodgson smoothed it against the windblown parapet, and peered.

'Goodness!' he exclaimed. 'It's from Jas. Rumbelow & Sons, Printers. They say that because I agreed to cut my chapter about the wiggy wasp out of my new book, it is now some four pages short, contra to the agreement of the something ultimo hereinunder referred to, and is taking bread out of their mouths!'

'New book?' said Scrimweasel, since some sort of reply seemed called for.

'*Through The Looking-Glass,*' said Dodgson.

Scrimweasel leered horribly.

'Never mind *Through The Looking-Glass*, squire,' he said nudging Dodgson's tea-stained waistcoat evilly, 'what you ought to do is *Through The Telescope*, know what I mean?'

'Do you really think so?' said Dodgson.

'You're a bit of a photographer,' said Scrimweasel, 'catch my drift?'

'Not exactly,' said Dodgson.

'Make a fortune,' said Scrimweasel. 'All this Victorian repression, you could clean up. Forty-eight poses, as seen from top of famous building by genuine connoisseur, sent under plain cover. I would,' he added, putting his small face up against the mathematician's left mutton-chop, 'be prepared to hold the magnesium, for a small consideration.'

'I am afraid,' said Dodgson, simultaneously snapping his hat open and his telescope shut with a single adroit flick, 'I have no time to think about that now. I am already late for poor Mr Rumbelow.'

Whereupon he sprang to the staircase, and clattered out of sight.

Scrimweasel stared after him.

'He's a fool to himself,' he said.

It was not, however, until four more days had passed that Dodgson found himself standing in Ludgate Hill, outside the premises of Jas. Rumbelow. True, he had arrived in London three days earlier, but it had been some time since he had visited the metropolis, and thus had his complicated senses ravished by its promise. Emerging from Paddington Station, he had joined a crocodile of small girls in captivating boaters and in consequence had spent the night accidentally locked in the Natural History Museum.

The second night, the locking had been somewhat more deliberate; but they had given him a cup of tea in the morning and, it having been explained that he was a famous author and therefore as mad as a hatter, they had returned his possessions to him, including the telescope, and sent him on his way. Unfortunately, he soon after stopped dead in the middle of the Strand to muse upon the madness of hatters, and was knocked over by a brewer's dray; he spent the third night in the London Hospital, but was found the following morning creeping through the fever ward in an attempt to photograph the smaller nurses, and was forcibly discharged.

'Well?' barked Jas. Rumbelow, as the vague figure wandered into the print shop.

'My name,' said Dodgson, 'is Dodgson.'

'How fascinating,' said Rumbelow. 'Well I never. Blow me. There's a thing. Well, Mr Dodgson, it's been a pleasure talking to you, but I have to get on now on account of being four days behind with some bloody—'

'It's him!' cried a compositor suddenly, scattering bright type. 'It's Carroll!'

The staff looked up.

Rumbelow cocked his head, as if downwind of game.

'Carroll?' he said, quietly. 'You said Dodgson.'

'I have,' murmured Dodgson, colouring, 'an assumed name.'

Rumbelow leaned him into the wall.

'I am not bleeding surprised,' he muttered. 'If I was you, I'd change 'em both to Jenkins and emigrate, before the lads get their 'ands on you!

'I do understand,' said Dodgson, 'I do apologise.'

'Stuck here four days,' cried Rumbelow, 'twiddling our thumbs, orders not touched, contracts going begging, people ringing up about wedding invitations, luggage labels, visiting cards, all nice easy stuff, all turned down, can't touch it, can I? Waiting on Mr Carroll, aren't I?'

'I'm sorry. I was held up.'

'Strung up'd be favourite,' said the compositor.

'Thirty-eight inches short, that book,' said Rumbelow. 'Bloody yard out, this one, Samuel. Calls himself a professional. Bloody yard short.'

Dodgson sighed.

'Well, I suppose it will just have to be a shorter book,' he said, 'that's all. We could have 188 pages instead of 192.'

They stared at him.

'I may have to sit down,' said Rumbelow.

'He's never heard of sections,' said the compositor.

'Don't they teach you nothing at Oxford?' said a tapper.

'They come in sections, books,' said Rumbelow, to Dodgson. 'Never mind pages, mate. They come in bunches of sixteen. How many sixteens in 188?'

'Calls himself a mathematician,' said the compositor.

'Could we not have four blank pages at the end?' enquired Dodgson.

'Oh my God!' said Rumbelow.

'We'd be a laughing-stock,' said the tapper.

'Bugger laughing-stock,' snapped the compositor. 'Any talk of blank pages, I'll have the lads straight out. Wouldn't surprise me if some of the machinery suddenly fell over, neither.'

'Maybe he'd like it done triangular,' said the tapper heavily. 'Nice triangular octavo. Fur endpapers, possibly.'

'Don't joke,' said Rumbelow, 'I remember this ratbag. He's the one what give us that Mouse's Tale in his last book. Bloody wossname, emblematic verse. Started off in fourteen-point, come wiggling down the page unregistered, ended up in bloody diamond-point at the bottom.'

'Never!' cried the compositor. 'Was that *him*? I was here all Whitsun over that. I had to get a draught off the apothecary on the Tuesday, I've never known bowels like it.'

'Oh dear,' said Dodgson, 'what should I do?'

'Bloody write another yard, is what,' said Rumbelow. 'You got twenty minutes. I'm not running into overtime.'

Dodgson blenched.

'One can't just dash it off, you know,' he protested.

'Oh, I see,' said Rumbelow. 'One would prefer to carry one's teeth away in one's hat, would one?'

Dodgson sighed.

'Well, I *do* happen to have a little poem I scribbled on the back of an old charge-sheet I found the other night,' he murmured, 'which I suppose I could pop in at the end of the first chapter. If that would be all right.'

'No problem,' said Rumbelow, 'if it goes to a yard, and no dodgy turns at the end of lines or nothing. Let's have it, then.'

Dodgson groped in his tail-coat pocket, and fished out a crumpled flimsy.

'I don't know how appropriate it is, mind,' he said. 'It's called *JANUARY.*'

'Very nice,' said Rumbelow. 'Straightforward.'

Dodgson cleared his throat.

' 'Twas chilly, and the slimy roads
Did shine and shimmer in the rain:
All misty were the birds' abodes,
And the cold grassy plain.

Beware of January, my son!
The hoar-frost's bite, the . . .'

'Yes, fine, lovely, terrific!' interrupted Rumbelow. 'We haven't got all bloody day, squire, give it here.'

He snatched the flimsy, and handed it to the tapper, who scuttled off to his stool, closely followed by the compositor.

Dodgson watched them go, nervously.

'Er . . .'

'You still here?' said Rumbelow.

'I was wondering,' murmured Dodgson, 'whether I would see a proof?'

'Do me a favour,' replied Rumbelow. 'We're a week behind as it is.'

'I just thought I'd enquire,' said Dodgson.

Oedipus Bruce

In Australia a recommendation was made recently that incest between a mother and son should no longer be illegal.

ACT ONE

Enter Chorus. They are citizens of Adelaide. They have corks dangling from their hats. They are all dead drunk.

CHORUS   Our mouths are like the inside of an abbo's trousers. We have all been walking through yesterday's lunch. We are as much use as an earwig's tit. What happened to last Wednesday?

Enter Barry, King of Adelaide, on all fours.

CHORUS   Hallo, Bazza, you look like two ton of old fish-heads.

BARRY   I've just been out in the fly box, saying goodbye to breakfast.

CHORUS   It's not like old Bazza to honk the bacon down the pipes after a night on the frosty tubes. Old Bazza has a gut like a ship's boiler. We have seen old Bazza sink ten gallons of Mrs Foster's Finest without threatening the drainage. Old Bazza must be upset about something.

BARRY   Too right! I was reading my horoscope in *Beer Weekly,* and it says where it's bad dos on the family scene this year, my flaming son is gonna flaming kill me, also beer could go up by as much as ten flaming cents a tube!

CHORUS   Stone the crows, Bazza! Ten cents a *tube*? This could spell the end of flaming civilisation as we flaming know it!

33

BARRY   Next thing you know, the supermarkets'll be charging corkage on flaming Parozone! I blame the Japs.

CHORUS   Too right. What's this about your son? We didn't know you had a son. We didn't realise you ever went near your old lady. Isn't she the sheila who looks like a '37 Holden pick-up, sounds like a drag-saw, and smells like a dead dingo?

BARRY   Time was. She's past her best now. Still, when a bloke's tied a few on of a Saturday night, it's no worse than cleaning the chimney in your bare feet. That's how we ended up with young Bruce. He's a bright little bastard, can't be more'n ten months old, and he's already been done twice for being in charge of a push-chair while unfit. I'll be sorry to see him go, straight up.

CHORUS   Go? What are you gonna do with him, Bazza?

BARRY   I'm not risking some flaming kid growing up and doing his daddy with a lead sock. I'm gonna drive him out to Broken Hill and nail him to the floor.

CHORUS   Good on yer, Bazza! Trouble with kids today, they need a firm hand. No flaming authority left. No sense of family. Good luck, Bazza, got to rush now or they'll be picking bits of bladder off the ceiling.

Exeunt.

ACT TWO

The outback, near Broken Hill. Enter King Barry, carrying Bruce, and Wayne, a shepherd. They are all drunk.

BARRY   There you go, Wayne, I've tied his flaming feet together, all you have to do is drop him in the sheep dip. Watch how you handle him, he can go off like a flaming mortar when he's had a few, we had to redecorate the entire bungalow once.

WAYNE   Count on me, Bazza, I'll pop him in the dippo when I go to fill up me bottles. I'm expecting a few blokes over this evening for a bit of a blast.

Exit Bazza. Wayne stands holding the baby for a moment or two, then falls down and begins snoring.

34

BRUCE   Burp.
Exit Bruce, crawling.

ACT THREE

Twenty years later. During this period, Bruce has been brought up as a sheep by an elderly ram and ewe who found him as a baby. He walks on two legs, but neither he nor his adoptive parents think this in any way odd. This is Australia. Bruce's diet has been grass and sheep dip. He is tall, strong, and permanently drunk, and has picked up a little English from the labels of the beer cans with which the outback is strewn.

It is a hot morning. Bruce is staggering along a dusty track, when he meets another man staggering towards him. The man is Craig, a brewing representative. He is drunk.

CRAIG   Stone the flaming crows, it's Bruce!

BRUCE   You got the wrong bloke, blue. My name's Sixteen Fluid Ounces. It was Pull Ring Here for a time, I'll give yer that, but it's never been flaming Bruce.

CRAIG   Well take it from me, cobber, it's Bruce now all right, they had your picture in *The Daily Beer*, and if you want my advice you'll keep away from your folks. It says in the paper that as sure as flies lay eggs in a wombat's trade-mark, you're gonna fill in your old man and marry your old lady!

BRUCE   Yeah, well, the bloke who wrote that never saw my old lady. She's got four black hooves and twelve nipples, not to mention some bloody peculiar personal habits. You'd think twice before jumping on a mattress with that.

CRAIG   Don't argue, mate, *The Daily Beer* never lies!

He falls down. Bruce hesitates for a time, then shrugs, sets his shoulders, turns his back resolutely on Broken Hill and takes instead the opposite direction, towards Adelaide.

ACT FOUR

The road near Adelaide. A battered truck is rattling along it, with King Barry at the wheel, lurching in every pot-hole and spilling old beer-cans at every yard. At the top of a little rise stands Bruce, albeit unsteadily. As the truck approaches, he thumbs it down. Barry looks out of the window.

35

BRUCE	Afternoon, sport. You wouldn't have a tube of Foster's aboard by any chance? I haven't eaten for six weeks.
BARRY	Well, now, blue, that's a very interesting question! A very interesting question indeed. Why not have it engraved on brass and shove it where the moon never shines, har, har, har!

At this, Bruce tears the door off, drags Barry out onto the road, and batters him lifeless with it. He removes eight cans of lager from the body, drains them, belches happily, climbs into the truck, and sets off on a zig-zag course, back towards Adelaide.

ACT FIVE: *Scene One*

A month later. Adelaide, before the royal palace. It is an attractive wooden bungalow with a pleasing neo-Georgian room-extension in primrose mock-stucco nailed to the front. There are five carriage lamps on the front door, and a gnome holding a sign that reads '38 to 38A Alopecia Avenue'. Enter Bruce, who pushes open the wrought-iron gate and rings a doorbell. The chimes of Viva España die away, the door opens.

BRUCE	Queen Glenda?
GLENDA	That's right. Sorry about the Marigold gloves, sport, I was just worming the cat. What can I do for you?
BRUCE	Promise you won't laugh, Glenda, only I met this sphinx up the road.
GLENDA	I know how it gets sometimes, blue. I usually get pink spiders running over the flaming sideboard.
BRUCE	No, straight up, Glenda, I met this sphinx and it said if I got three riddles right I could come round here and marry you. I didn't have anything else on this morning, so I thought, what the hell, it's better than a poke in the eye with a sharp stick!

Enter Chorus, supporting one another.

CHORUS	He'll be flaming sorry he said that!

Exeunt, on hands and knees.

GLENDA	So you answered the riddle all right, then?
BRUCE	I don't know. The sphinx was legless. It was all he could do to give me your address before he fell over.
GLENDA	I swear they put something in it up the factory.

When I was a girl, you could drink thirty-one pints before breakfast.

They marry. The wedding reception goes on for nine weeks. At the end of it, the bungalow has disappeared beneath a pyramid of beer cans. A number of guests are dead.

Scene Two

Some of the cans clatter to the ground. Bruce emerges from the gap, obviously distressed. He has a stick up his nose. Enter Norman, a neighbour. He is drunk.

NORMAN   Stone the flaming crows, Bruce, what's that stick doing up your conk?

BRUCE   I've been trying to poke me flaming eyes out, Norm. I can't seem to get the flaming range. I guess I'll have to wait till I'm flaming sober.

NORMAN   You don't want to go poking yer eyes out, mate. They'll rob you blind up the off-licence. It could cost a flaming bomb! What made you think of it?

BRUCE   I found out Glenda's me mum, Norm. I've only gone and married me flaming mummy!

NORMAN   No cause to pop yer headlights, blue! Mind, I can see it could be a bit awkward. Been a few naughties, have there?

BRUCE   Nothing like that, Norm. Nothing of that order. I haven't been capable, for one thing. Glenda says they put something in up the factory. No, it's giving up the bungalow, Norm. You spend twenty years as a flaming sheep, suddenly you got gas central heating and three flaming low-flush pastel suites, it's not easy to give it all up just like that.

NORMAN   Strikes me you're being a bit previous, cobber. I can't see why you and Glenda can't make a go of it. She's a very nice woman when she's drunk and no beard to speak of.

BRUCE   But it's against the flaming law, Norm!

NORMAN   Then they'll have to flaming change it, mate!

BRUCE   Would they do that, Norm?

NORMAN   Would they . . . ? You just come down the pub with me, cobber, we'll wake up the Home Secretary and put it to him straight!

Exeunt. Enter Chorus, dragging one another.
CHORUS   In Australia, all is flaming possible! In Australia, a
         new world is flaming born! In Australia, I flaming
         will! In Australia . . .
They collapse. They lie there. They snore.

CURTAIN

May the Force be with You

'A pushbutton system for checking criminal records at Scotland Yard starts today. It means saving time on manual searches and reduces the vast amount of paperwork, weighing several tons, which make up existing records.

The Police National Computer will also begin operating with the wanted and missing persons index, with the object of speedily answering enquiries from police forces all over the country.'—Daily Telegraph

EVENING ALL!

Well, that about wraps it up for another week. You'll be glad to know that we got the Archbishop of York for the Gillingham bank job, and it came as a considerable relief to all concerned, I don't mind saying! And Mr and Mrs Arnold Harmsworth, formerly of the Golden Sunset Retired Gentlefolks Home, Tunbridge Wells, will shortly be removing to Parkhurst and Holloway, if I'm any judge, as the result of the tip-off our PNC received from the Interpol computer which conclusively established them as the kidnappers of millionaire Italian child ventriloquist Seamus Dooley.

As for poor old Mrs Doreen Clittermole of Dock Green TV Rentals, her little dog Chummy turned up within minutes of her informing us of his disappearance. It transpired that he was living in the Bellavista Hotel, Willesden, with his common-law wife Gerald; an interesting sidelight on the affair is that when, as a matter of routine procedure, we patched Gerald's VAT number into our computer, it took less than half an hour for him to receive delivery of twelve hundred tons of prime quality anthracite and a contract from ATV for a thirteen-part series based on the life of George XIV.

You'll all be wondering, I've no doubt, about the gun found

at the scene of the Murchison Jig & Tool payroll raid. Well, it turned out that the villains had forgotten to take the elementary precaution of filing off the number! So we popped it into the computer, and by two o'clock that same afternoon it had been established as the property of the *Oxford University Press*, a tanker plying between Rangoon and Maracaibo. Montreal Mounted Police have been alerted, and when the ship turns up in Rome, there are going to be a few red faces at Huddersfield Town Hall, I can tell you!

Mind you, it hasn't all been plain sailing on that case, ha-ha, pardon my little pun! You'll remember that we found the getaway car abandoned outside Ramsgate? Well, we linked our PNC to the Vehicle Registration Computer at Swansea, and it transpired that there are actually 13,244 cars with the licence number BEC 21C, all of them—and here's the queer part—all of them owned by our old friend the Archbishop of York! Now, all right, I can hear you saying, all right, here is a known villain, got a lot of form, it is clearly on the cards that he might have nicked 13,244 cars and made the mistake of giving them all the same number-plate. After all, look at last week, when the entire Godfrey Davis Van Hire Fleet turned out to have been nicked by Barclaycard, you wouldn't think a big outfit like Barclaycard would knock off an entire fleet of commercial vehicles and then make the elementary mistake of keeping them over a shop in Clerkenwell Road, would you?

Well, yes, is the short answer, *we* would, and that's what separates us professionals from, if you'll forgive me, all you well-meaning amateur detectives out there! The whole point is that Barclaycard *is* a big operation, employs thousands of villains, it only takes one slip by one villain who happens not to have his mind on the job, and Bob's your uncle! But the Archbishop of York is not a big operation, he could not handle 13,244 hot motor-cars, and anyway, his *modus operandi*, as we call it in the trade, is doing banks.

So what's the answer? Is the *Oxford University. Press* trying to frame the Archbishop of York for the Murchison Jig & Tool job? Not quite so simple, I'm afraid; real life is a bit different from what you good people see in the cinema! No, we in the Force have to take an entirely different tack; if we're going to get to the bottom of cases like this, we have to start from the other end: by great good fortune, or perhaps I should say, rather, with great foresight, the numbers of all the notes stolen in the raid had been punched into the Bank of England computer. Within, quite literally, seconds of our linking the three computers together, Swansea's, the Bank's, and our own, and feeding in the note numbers and the 13,244 identical license numbers, we had succeeded in diverting all incoming Heathrow flights to Darjeeling.

As Chief Superintendent Fosket, who is in charge of the case, told the press that evening: 'We now know one thing for sure. Behind this whole operation there is a Mister Big. Find him, and you've got the thing sewn up in a nutshell!'

It's now only a matter of time.

Meanwhile, what about those two lads we found stripping the lead off the roof of St. Swine's?

Well, we put a fingerprint check on them through the computer, and I think you might be mildly interested by the upshot! Turns out they have been wanted for sixty-nine years for the murder in Hilldrop Crescent, Islington, of one Belle Crippen. Newspapers at the time made much of the fact that a Miss Ethel le Neve escaped to the USA dressed as a boy, a cunning ploy but one you might well expect from someone who has managed to keep out of the law's hands for best part of a century. Still, chummy always makes a mistake sooner or later, and hers was turning up on the church roof last February! No, friends, the Yard never closes a file. Mind you, Ethel is no longer a young woman; as a matter of fact, she is no longer an old woman, either. But, as the Inspector commented when we got her down to Dock Green and had a good look, a lot can happen in seventy years; still, just to be on the safe side, we got the PNC to tie in with the Somerset House computer, and it bore out all our suspicions. The suspect was down as one Ngo Mbibi, divorced forty-three times and killed at Vimy Ridge.

As I said, a very devious young woman indeed!

So there we are, another week gone, another slice of criminal life wrapped up, another few lads up for Queen's Commendations. The head found in the Mole Street public lavatory turned out to belong to the Norwich Union Insurance Company, Ronald Biggs was indeed proved to be innocent of all charges, it having been established that he was playing in the Wimbledon Singles Final at the time, and the round-up of all Access cardholders in Greater London to assist us with our enquiries into the nobbling of the Bakerloo Line automatic points switching system was brought at last to a successful conclusion.

Oh yes, nearly forgot! The Uxbridge rapist did not escape the full consequences of his appalling action, either, and has now received a gas bill for £438,000,000.00.

Thanks for listening, everyone!

And mind how you go.

Spring Hopes Eternal

IT WAS DARK in No. 6 Shaft of Bolsover Colliery, as it had every right to be. Three thousand feet above my borrowed helmet as the crow burrowed, Spring was bursting in a barrage of sexual pyrotechnics: wheeling birds thwacked in mid-air with the ringing accuracy of those who know their lust to be seasonally momentary; frogs clung to one another with that quiet desperation which renders the sexual comedy poignant; rabbits were shooting from their holes like soft cannonballs, hungry for collision; a billion worms, by nature hermaphrodite, were making their agonising snap decisions; and even the flowers were at it like knives.

But down here, all was dark, mineral, sterile. An eon back, these trees were fecund with hot sap; now, they were mere fused corpses, silently awaiting the ultimate degradation of the Phurnacite mould. Sobering environs for a boy of not yet forty summers: I, too, when geophysics had taken its slow and grisly course, should end up crackling in someone's grate, ten million years hence, kindling clichés in his head as he gazed, dreaming, at my hissing encarboned elbow.

I sighed.

'Oh Gawd,' said a weary voice, 'Mortality weighs heavily on him like unwilling sleep.'

I peered. The gloom yielded nothing.

'I beg your pardon?' I said.

'Keats,' said the voice. 'People come down a mine, first thing you know they're going on about man's brief span etcetera. Wet in the extreme, people.'

My eyes were by this time accustomed to the dark; the shaft was empty. I raised the cage, and looked at the canary.

'It is no good,' said the voice, 'looking at the canary. They are ignorant little bleeders. They go gentle into that good night, as

43

Dylan put it. Thick as two short planks is how one might sum up your average canary. It is no use expecting them to talk. Cheep, cheep, then it falls off its little perch, stone dead. Your budgerigar, faced with methane, would not pop its clogs without considerable verbal protest, even if it was only *Who's a dead boy, then?* Canaries deserve all they get.'

'I'm sorry,' I said, 'I'm afraid I can't see you.'

'Brace yourself,' said the voice. 'I am up here on the ceiling.'

I glanced up, and my helmet-beam followed the glance.

I dropped the cage.

I grasped a pit-prop for support.

I may have croaked something.

'Yes,' said the voice, 'one does not run into four-foot dragonflies every day of the week. However,' it continued, unplucking itself from the roof and dropping to the floor beside me, 'we do not, contrary to popular myth, sting people. Mind you, we embrace our prey and suck it to death, so it is six of one and half a dozen of the other if you happen to be odontata-fodder, but as human beings are not, I fail to see what all the staggering and gasping is about.'

I licked my lips; slowly, reason papered over the shattered machismo. A sort of reason, anyway.

'You are not,' I said, 'quite what I expected. I saw this story in the *Daily Telegraph*, and being of an inquiring nature, I . . .'

'A good paper,' said the dragonfly, 'excellent foreign coverage.'

'It said you were a fossil.'

'Excellent foreign coverage,' repeated the dragonfly, 'but not the first bloody idea when it comes to natural history.'

'Are you in fact the world's oldest dragonfly?' I enquired, a question which, when I first embarked upon the slippery slopes of Fleet Street, I had never imagined I should someday put.

'Probably,' it replied. 'I look after myself. Careful diet, no nasty habits, plenty of fresh air, all that. Yes, I go back a bit. Coleridge,' it continued, 'couldn't half swat. I nearly didn't make it out of the Regency, you know. He'd have his work cut out now, though, wouldn't he'

It laughed, at a guess. A strange sound, just beyond description, I'm afraid.

'Yes,' I said, 'you are somewhat large, for a dragonfly.'

' 'Course I am, son, 'course I am. I've had the time.'

'And, er, surprisingly articulate.'

'In several languages, though I says it as shouldn't. Were you, for example, a Jap, we'd be nattering away in Nipponese like nobody's business, swopping Jap jokes, all that. Or Swahili, French, Norse, you name it. I've been about, son. I have stood on Thomas Mann's window-sill before now. Ferdinand de Lesseps once pointed me out to his uncle. I also,' and here it nudged me, an experience, given the choice, I should have declined, 'know the identify of Jack the Ripper. But I am not letting on.'

'I see,' I lied.

'It would involve,' said the dragonfly, 'betraying a lady's confidence.'

'Ah.'

'You have to remember,' said the dragonfly, 'I grew up at a time when such considerations were not treated with derision. Call me,' it murmured, 'old-fashioned, if you will.'

'No, no!' I cried, 'I should not dream of it.'

'The world,' said the dragonfly, fixing me with its thousand-faceted eye, 'is going up the spout, in my considered view. Punk rock, soya substitute, nylon carpeting, Kerry Packer, aluminium skis, gay lib, bingo, soft bog-paper, electric toothbrushes. And as for this new Dennis Potter rubbish . . .'

'You have obviously,' I said, 'a thoughtful turn of a mind for an, er . . .'

'Insect, yes. Do not show your appalling ignorance, son. If you turn to volume seven of the *Encyclopaedia Britannica*, page 623 as I recall, you will find the following perceptive remark: "The dragonfly's life is encompassed and guided by vision. It is, however, a mosaic vision." How about *that* for openers?'

'I did indeed read it up before coming down here,' I said. 'I thought the mosaic vision referred to merely concerned the structure of . . .'

The dragonfly turned its bizarre eye upon me again. It glittered like those mirrored orbs that turn slowly above Mecca dance-floors.

'We have already established,' it said, menacingly soft, 'just how much you bloody know about people of the hexapod persuasion.' It turned its huge blue head away from the lamplight. 'Mosaic vision,' it murmured. 'One sees all, one knows all, one is in full possession of the route concerning the Promised Land, one is doomed to stand upon the sidelines and watch the human scrimmage kick itself to ruination. It is,' said the world's oldest dragonfly, 'one of the reasons I am down the bleeding pit.'

'I was going to ask you about that,' I said.

' 'Course you were, son, 'course you were,' said the dragonfly patiently. 'That is all journalism is, nowadays. Do you hope for a peaceful settlement, despite your enormous tits do you one day hope to become a serious actress, why do you think your book about an underwater vet is top of the best-seller lists, is there any truth in the rumour that you have signed to open the batting for Saudi Arabia, what is your view of the uncertainty regarding the dollar as of this moment in time, just how *much* of a threat is Concorde to the Heavyside Layer? We have come a long way,' muttered the dragonfly, 'from W. T. Stead and Geoffrey Dawson and C. P. Scott and Nat Gubbins. I have had,' it continued, tapping my knee with a fearful foreleg, 'four million sexual couplings of one kind and another. Have you any idea of the disgusting fight there would be in what presently calls itself Fleet Street were I to put my memoirs on the open market?'

'*Four million?*'

'Give or take. I stopped counting after the 1851 Exhibition. The dragonfly has the right attitude to sex, son: the act takes place at a combined velocity of sixty miles per hour. There is consequently no time for unseemly mucking about, no groping behind bus shelters and similar, no post-coital mooning, no doubts concerning impending impotence or multiple orgasm, no discussion of who is treating whom as a sex object, no bogus mysticism elevating simple genetic mechanics beyond their basic significance, no guilt, no fear, no interminable magazine articles or panel discussions—in rather more than three million of my own encounters I did not even have time to catch the name of my beloved.' It sighed, I felt. A sort of melancholy exhalation through the scales. 'That is another reason I am down here. There is no fun in anything any more.'

'When,' I asked, 'did you retire to this pit?'

'Christmas,' replied the dragonfly. 'I had been thinking

about it for some time, mind. What finally persuaded me, I cannot exactly put a name to—no illuminated angels in Regent Street, possibly, the failure of the Rhodesian initiative, perhaps, the fact that bits were falling off Morris Marinas all over the world, the pitiful inadequacy of the Sadat peace plan, the revaluation of the green pound, the rise of Billy Carter, the announcement of ITV's spring schedules, Dutch elm disease, the Horn of Africa, Margaret Thatcher, the Socialist Workers Party, Roddy Llewellyn . . . who can say?'

'Will you never return to the surface?'

It spread four of its legs expressively, balancing brilliantly on the remaining two.

'What point is there?' it cried. 'The world is too much with us, late and soon—a fool, Wordsworth, but nobody to touch him when it came to moaning, I used to watch him stare at mud, it was an education, I don't mind saying. I have had life up to here, son. I shall remain in the pit, with my memories. It is the most sensible course.'

'That may be true,' I said. 'However, today is March 21st.'

'So?'

'It is the first day of Spring,' I said.

The world's oldest dragonfly turned its amazing eye upon me once again. The gleaming facets, if I was not mistaken, had lost a little of their diamantine cynicism.

'Oh, bloody hell, all right!' it said, irritably. 'But I'm only coming up for a bit, mind.'

Life mit Vater

A man claiming to be one of Adolf Hitler's sons has turned up in France, intending to sell his memoirs. One of the other ones has not been slow to follow.

I WAS BORN on January 18, 1923, at 17, Bolitha Villas, SE26.

It was an ordinary little Sydenham terraced house, flanked to the left by Dunlookin, and to the right by Fredberyl. Ours was called Arbeit Macht Frei.

It was distinguishable from the rest only by virtue of its paintwork. The front door was puce, the downstairs windows were yellow, and the upstairs were variously blue, green and beige. They were painted thus by my father, this being his trade; but he was constantly going abroad on business, leaving the job partially done, and finding upon his return that the paint in the open pots had gone hard.

He would then throw the pots at my mother and run up and down Bolitha Villas in his bare feet shrieking that the Jews had left the lids off. By evening, he had invariably calmed down, and would be found, weeping, in the shed, muttering that he had gone off beige, or blue, or eau-de-nil, or whatever it happened to be. Towards midnight, I would be awoken by the strains of Wagner, and would tiptoe to the window and stare out towards the shed, through the tiny window of which I would be able to see my father in a flaxen wig beating the cat with the flat of his wooden sword.

Years later, recalling such memories, I asked my mother what had attracted her to him in the first place. She explained that she had met him at a dance in Leytonstone, where he was the only man in a helmet; halfway through the evening, he took the head of a conga line and marched it nine miles to

Dagenham, in driving hail. She was, she said, carried away by his natural authority. He also had a lighter side, she maintained, and was well known, before his broody period set in, for his impressions of Charlie Chaplin.

None of this, of course, was known to me in my childhood, and my father remained, in consequence, something of a puzzle. I did not, for example, know why he slept on the roof in all weathers, and I was acutely embarrassed, being but four years old, when he took me to the Natural History Museum and insisted on goose-stepping to the bus-stop. He also, when we arrived, screamed at the dinosaur skeleton for some minutes on the grounds, as I recall, that it had given up without a struggle. He calmed down somewhat upon the arrival of three uniformed attendants, pausing only to inspect their buttons, feel their biceps, and pat them on the head affectionately, before taking me away to look at a stuffed gorilla beside which he delivered, to my total incomprehension, a long lecture about the decadence of jazz.

That Christmas, an aunt gave me a golliwog, which my father hanged. When I asked him why, he jumped out of the window.

In the spring of 1929, on my father's insistence, I joined the Cubs.

Although, initially, I was a figure of derision (I was the only one in a brown shirt; and also, try as I might, I could not fully disguise the fact that my cap had a spike on it), before long my little playmates were treating me with more and more respect. This was largely on account of my accoutrements; each time my daddy returned home from one of his foreign trips, he would bring me a new piece of equipment, until, by midsummer, I was turning up at meetings in riding-boots, Sam Browne belt and a gas-mask, carrying a Schmeisser machine-pistol. Where other boys wore cheap blunt penknives on their belts, I wore a grenade pouch; where they sported a woodcraft badge, I bore the Iron Cross.

Akela, our leader, was very decent about it: not only was she trained in the Montessori method, and thus responsive to self-expression irrespective of its prime motive, she also had steel

49

spectacles gummed together at their broken bridge, thinning hair, a concave bust, and legs like Indian clubs. When my father, therefore, clasped her to him on collecting me one evening, kissed her on both sallow cheeks, and informed her that she would be the flower of the New Sydenham, a mottled glow suffused her entire visible surface.

Thereafter, I could do no wrong. When, the following week, I led my patrol away from its ostensible mission to pluck four-leaf clovers on Sydenham Hill and took them instead on a house-to-house search of Dulwich looking for Bolshevik printing presses, she awarded me the Blue Max with Oak Leaves and Crossed Swords, and allowed me to blow her whistle.

There is no guessing the heights to which I might have risen, had it not been for a characteristically over-enthusiastic blunder on my father's part. That autumn, our group went away to weekend camp. My parents took me down in our old Morris Ten, my mother driving and my father standing on the seat beside her with his head and shoulders poking up through the sunshine roof. Upon our arrival, my father dismounted and, catching sight of the tented camp, immediately began encircling it with a roll of barbed wire he always carried in the boot.

It was while he was attempting to construct a makeshift searchlight tower by lashing one of the Morris's headlamps to a telephone pole that an assistant to the Chief Scout ran up and insisted that he come down and explain his behaviour.

Daddy then threw himself to the ground and began biting the grass. Soon afterwards, we received a brief note informing us that Sydenham Cub Pack 1374 was being reconstituted under new leadership and that my membership of the group would not be looked upon with favour.

Of the subsequent career of Akela, I have little first-hand information: between her departure from SE26 in 1929 and her suicidal single-handed attack on General Vasilevsky's 4th Armoured Division outside Stalingrad, history has drawn a disappointing blank.

For two years thereafter, I saw little of my father. There had been some local unpleasantness on Guy Fawkes' Night 1929 when, by dint of a nocturnal raid on the files of Sydenham Public Library, he managed to steal enough tickets to allow him to take out its entire stock, which he then piled in our back yard and ignited, having first topped the heap with a stuffed effigy of Issy Bonn; and as the result of this he once more left the country.

Apart from one notorious flying visit to Bolitha Villas in the winter of 1930, when he showed up proudly on the arm of an aristocratic English girl—it ended in chaos when she laughed at our three china ducks and Daddy in consequence attempted to garotte Mummy with his armband—I did not see him again until late on Midsummer's Day, 1931.

It is an occasion which remains embossed upon my memory, despite the passage of almost fifty years.

I was coming home from school, and upon turning into Bolitha Villas from Pondicherry Crescent, I noticed a large crowd outside Fredberyl. Most of them were neighbours, but there were policemen in the crowd, too, and a fire-engine was drawn up at the kerb. Fredberyl being the house next to Arbeit Macht Frei, I was therefore amazed, upon drawing nearer, to see my father at an upstairs window of it, shrieking and waving a makeshift flag.

'What's going on?' I enquired of an elderly police sergeant, whom I had met when my father, during one of his many bursts of wild enthusiasm, had written to Scotland Yard applying for a submarine licence.

'It's your old man,' he replied. 'He has annexed Fredberyl. As I understand it, he intends to knock down the dividing wall and use the combined premises for a spring offensive against Dunlookin.'

Being only eight, I could not of course grasp the full implications of the situation; I was, however, understandably concerned for the welfare of my father.

'Oh dear!' I cried. 'What will happen to my daddy? Will you have to go in there and drag him out and all that?'

The sergeant stared down at me in some irritation.

'*Me?*' he said. 'Intervene in a domestic wossname? You must be joking, son! I don't know what your old man's got against Fredberyl and Dunlookin, but one thing's for bleeding sure, I have not come all the way here from Tulse Hill to interfere in a

51

quarrel in a faraway street between people of whom I know nothing.'

Doctor No will see You Now

'*CIA agents who lose the qualities that make good spies are retired at fifty under special pensions, according to testimony yesterday before a House Intelligence Sub-Committee. "A 70-year-old James Bond is kind of hard to imagine," said Republican Senator Sam Stratton.*'—Herald Tribune

BOND TENSED IN THE DARKNESS, and reached for his teeth.

There was something in the room.

You did not train for fifty-three years without developing that imponderable acuity that lay beyond mere observation. Indeed, you found that as the years went by, this sixth sense came, perforce, to replace the others: these days, he could hear dog-whistles, with or without his batteries in.

At least, he assumed they were dog-whistles. Nobody else seemed to hear them.

The teeth fell exactly to hand, there between the senna and the Algipan on his bedside table. He waited a calculated split-second for the cement to cleave snugly to his palate. It felt good. It should have: it was made for him by Chas. Fillibee of Albemarle Street, the world's premier fixative man. Senior British agents had been going to Fillibee since before the War; he knew their special requirements. When Witherspoon 004 had gone into the London Clinic to have his prostate done and the KGB had taken the opportunity to lob an Ostachnikov nuclear mortar into his grape-box, the only thing left intact between Baker Street Station and the Euston underpass had been Witherspoon's upper plate.

Very carefully, Bond slid his hand beneath his pillow and closed it around the ribbed butt of his Walther PPK 9mm Kurz with the custom-enlarged trigger guard by Rinz of Stuttgart which allowed the arthritic knuckle of Bond's forefinger to slide smoothly around the trigger. His other hand took the light switch.

In one smooth, practised move, Bond snapped on the light switch and simultaneously peered around the room.

There was a shadowy, half-familiar figure by the dressing table. Bond fired, twice, the fearful reports cracking back and forth between the walls, and the figure reeled.

'So much,' murmured Bond coolly, 'for Comrade Nevachevski!'

Miss Moneypenny sat up in bed, her grizzled bun unravelling, her elegant muffler in fetching disarray.

'You silly old sod,' she said.

Bond beamed, deafly.

'Yes, wasn't it?' he said. 'Inch or so wide, mind, should've been straight between the eyes, but, my God, he didn't even have time to draw!'

'YOU'VE SHOT YOUR WIG-STAND!' shouted Miss Moneypenny. She stuck an ephedrine inhaler in her left nostril, and sucked noisily.

Bond put on his bi-focals.

'Ah,' he said. He brightened. 'Still a bloody good shot, though, eh?'

'I should cocoa,' said Moneypenny. 'It ricocheted off the hot-water bottle. God alone knows what it's done to your rubber sheet.'

'Bloody hell,' said Bond.

He switched the light out again, and lay back. As always, after untoward events, his wheeze was bad, crackling round the room like crumpling cellophane.

'Shall I rub you in?' murmured Moneypenny softly, from her distant cot.

'Don't start,' said Bond.

Moneypenny sighed. At sixty-eight, it seemed, her virginity was moving slowly but surely beyond threat.

Bond shuffled nonchalantly into M's office and tossed his hat in a neat arc towards the polished antler. The hat fell in the waste-bin. 007 stared at it for a time, and finally decided against

54

picking it up. On the last occasion upon which he had attempted a major stoop, it had taken four osteopaths to unwind him.

'Good morning,' said M, 'if you're from Maintenance, I'd like you to know that the roller towel is getting harder and harder to tug. I don't know what they're doing with them these days. I think they put something in them at the factory. When I was a lad, you could pull them down between thumb and forefinger. Possibly the KGB has a hand in it. Also, I have great difficulty in pulling the soap off that magnetic thingy.'

'It's me, sir,' said Bond, '00—'

He frowned.

M stared at him glaucously from nonagenarian eyes.

Bond took off his James Lobb galosh, and removed a slip of paper.

'7,' he said. '007.'

M trembled suddenly. He tugged at a drawer, but it did not budge.

'I've got a gun in here somewhere,' he said. 'By God, you'll know it when I find it! You're not 007, you swine, I've known 007 fifty years, he's bright ginger!'

'I shot my wig,' said Bond, gloomily.

M relaxed.

'No good getting angry with a wig,' he said. 'It's only doing its job.'

'You sent for me,' said Bond.

'In the CIA,' murmured M, 'I'd have been retired forty years ago. I would have one of those thermal pools with a thing that makes waves in it. I would have my own genito-urinary man coming in on a weekly basis. A TV hanging from the ceiling, mink linings for the cold snap, a hollow cane with Remy Martin in it, a rare dog.'

'About this job,' said Bond.

M blew his nose, ineptly.

'Usual thing,' he said. 'MIRV-launching Russian satellite has been brought down by a defecting Albanian inter-galactic tail-gunner in the pay of the Irgun Zwei Leomi. As you would expect, it has fallen down inside Vesuvius: crack KGB, CIA, Mafia, Triad, and IRA teams are already racing to the spot. I promised the PM we'd send our best man.'

'Oh, good,' muttered Bond. 'You don't think Snuggley might fit the bill better?'

'003?' said M. 'His leg's gone in for its annual service. No, James, it's you—bags of parachuting, ski-ing, scuba-diving, unarmed combat, all that, right up your street.'

'Quite,' said Bond.

'Pop along and see Charlie in Special Equipment,' said M.

'This,' said Charlie, 'is probably the most advanced truss in the world.'

'It's snug,' said Bond. 'What are all these pockets for?'

'Spare surgical stockings,' said Charlie, ticking off his fingers, 'international pensions book, collapsible alloy crutches, Sanatogen capsules, arch supports, emergency pee bottle, mittens, underwater deaf-aid, thermal liberty bodice, and a handbell in case you fall over somewhere and can't get up.'

'Super,' said Bond.

'Also,' said Charlie, 'we've been over your Morris Traveller and, ha-ha, tarted it up a bit. Apart from the fact that you'll now be able to get it up to fifty-five—'

'Christ!'

'—there's an emergency inertia brake that brings it to a dead stop in the event of the driver having a heart attack, plus two big orange lights on stalks in both wings enabling you to drive it through narrow spaces, a foot-button that throws your window out instantly in the event of nausea, an inflatable anti-haemorrhoid ring set in the driver's seat that activates at the first scream, and a 3× magnifying windshield that enables you to read road signs without getting out òf the car.'

'Fantastic,' muttered Bond.

'Good luck, 007,' said Charlie, 'and good hunting!'

He shook Bond's hand, but gently.

Bond nosed forward out of the roundabout, onto the Dover road.

People hooted.

The Traveller lurched forward, stalled, lurched on again.

007 ground into third gear. He glanced in his mirror, for the tenth time. Somebody was following him. They had been following him since Blackheath, almost two hours ago.

At the next traffic light, Bond got out, and walked back.

'I don't sell off the float, grandpa,' said the milkman.

'Why have you been following me?' said Bond levelly.

'I got no option, have I?' said the milkman. 'First off, we're the only two vehicles doing fifteen miles a wossname, second off, every time I bleeding pull out to overtake, you start wandering all over the road.'

'Evasive action,' snapped 007. 'Don't tell me you weren't trying to force me into the ditch. You're with SMERSH, right?'

The milkman took his cap off.

'It says Unigate on here,' he said.

'Ha!' cried Bond, and sprang into a Nakusai karate crouch, his left hand a club, his right fingers a dagger.

The milkman got out and helped him up.

'It's this knee I've got,' said Bond.

'Shouldn't be out, old geezer like you,' said the milkman. 'It's freezing.'

Bond laughed one of his short dry laughs. Once, men had gone white at the very sound.

'Be warm enough, soon, eh? I trust you're bound for Vesuvius?'

The milkman looked at him.

'I got Mafeking Crescent to do, and a bulk yoghurt up the telephone exchange,' he said, 'then I'm off home for *Pebble Mill.*'

'A likely story!' cried Bond. 'What's under that moustache, you Chinese bastard?'

007 made a lightning grab at the milkman's upper lip, misjudged the distance, and caught his forefinger in his opponent's mouth. The milkman closed his teeth on Bond's frail knuckle, and the agent fell back into the road. As he lay there, a bus-driver walked up, stood on him absently, and said to the milkman.

'These bleeding lights have gone green twice, sunshine.'

'Don't blame me,' said the milkman, 'this old bugger stuck his hand in my gob.'

The bus-driver glanced down.

'It's this ten pounds Christmas bonus they're getting,' he said. 'It's driving 'em all barmy. They've been smoking on the downstairs deck all morning.' He bent down, and hauled Bond upright. 'Come on, uncle, I'll see you across to the Whelk & Banjo.'

He took Bond into the public bar, and sat him on a stool, and went out again.

Bond took five pills. His hand was shaking, his heart was pounding, there was a tic in his right eye, and his bronchitis was coming back. He ought to get on, it was four clear days to Naples, given that he refused to drive at night and wanted to pop into the clinic at Vitry-le-François for his monthly check-up.

But, then again, was it worth it? The KGB might hit him, the CIA might shout at him if he couldn't keep up, his surgical skis were as yet untested, and as for swimming the Bay of Naples, he had noticed in himself of late an unsettling tendency to sink. Added to all of which, his SMERSH counterpart was a big Balinese stripper fifty years his junior, and he doubted that his current sexual techniques would persuade her to defect, given that he preferred doing it in his herringbone overcoat these days, apart from the fact that he had last performed a mere eight months before and seriously doubted whether his forces were yet in a position to be remustered.

It wasn't a bad pub, all in all, thought Bond. He could write out a report from here, elaborating a bit. After all, what could they expect for fifty quid a week after stoppages?

The barman looked up at Bond's cough.

'What'll it be?' he said.

'I'll have a small Wincarnis,' said Bond. He took off his balaclava. 'Shaken, not stirred.'

A Small Thing but Minoan

'We can be quite precise about the date. 4,000 years ago in Crete, during the Middle Minoan Period, linear writing in pen and ink was born.'—Fodor Guide to Crete

AGOROPHON SQUINTED UP at the noonday sun. It gonged down out of a brass sky; the arid rock baked; insects gasped, crept slowly for the shade of crevices.

'Beats me why you dragged me all the way out here,' he said irritably. 'Day like this, what you want is your feet in a basin and a bird standing behind you with a large frond.'

'I've got something to show you,' said Memnos. 'It's private.'

Agorophon looked at him.

'It's not that rash again, is it?' he said.

Memnos shook his head. He groped down inside the neckline of his smock, while his friend watched uneasily.

'There you are,' said Memnos, handing him a fragment of dried leaf, 'have a butcher's at that.'

'If it's a scab,' said Agorophon, 'I'm not going near it.'

'It's a leaf,' said Memnos, 'it's got something written on it.'

'*Written* on it?' cried Agorophon. 'How can you chisel a leaf?'

But he looked at it.

'You're right,' he said, at last. 'Squiggles. What a miraculous thing Nature is!'

'It's not natural,' replied Memnos. '*I* did it. I did it with ink.'

'Ink?'

'It's something I made from roots.'

'I thought that was gin,' said Agorophon.

'Different roots,' said Memnos. 'You don't drink this one.'

'Pity,' said Memnos. 'You can have enough of gin, this weather.'

59

'You write with it,' said Memnos. 'You dip a twig in it, and write.'

'Get off!' cried Agorophon. He looked at the leaf again. 'All right, what does it say?'

'It says X. P. Memnos, Number 9a, High Street.'

'What's it for?'

Memnos shrugged.

'It's all I could think of. You could give it to people. It's better than carrying a bagful of them stone visiting cards. Also, you can just dash 'em off. Instead of sitting there all day with a mallet.'

'Easier on the thumbs,' said Agorphon, 'I'll give you that.'

Memnos looked away from his friend, out over the broiling landscape, feeling faintly hollow. Disappointed wasn't quite the word. But, then, what was? The Cretan vocabulary was small, detailed, a lot of synonyms for food, weapons, internal organs, not much more. Perhaps it would expand, now, with the tedium of chiselling gone.

'Mind you,' said Agorophon, breaking into his reverie, 'I'll be glad to see the back of cuneiform, I don't mind saying. I could never make head nor tail out of it, it was just triangles. If we'd stuck with hieroglyphs, I could have got somewhere. I could have made something of myself. I used to enjoy reading hieroglyphs, all them little parrots, frogs, titchy houses, all that. I don't know why they gave it up.'

'Progress,' said Memnos.

'Yes, well,' said Agorophon.

Memnos frowned down at his leaf.

'I wonder what I ought to write first?' he murmured.

'Make marvellous betting slips,' said Agorophon.

'Very interesting,' said Old Memnos, looking disparagingly at the leaf. 'When are you going to go out and earn a living?'

'I want to be a writer,' said his son.

'What kind of work is that for a man?' said his mother. She dropped a rabbit's head into the pot, stirred it absently. 'I see them sitting in the square every day, hammering tablets, covered in dust. Labourers is what they are.'

'But this is a very fast system,' protested her son. He dipped his twig in a vial of murky liquid, and dashed off his address, ten times over, on a large piece of goatskin.

'Hang on!' shouted Old Memnos. 'She was making me a vest out of that!'

'It's got our address on it now,' said his son. 'That's another valuable asset.'

'I doubt whether you could market *that*,' said his mother. 'I don't see where there's much call for addressed underwear.'

'If you got run over,' said her son, 'they'd know where to bring you.'

His mother sniffed.

'About the only thing *I* can think of,' she said, 'is shopping lists. With stone shopping lists, time you've chiselled *Two kilograms brussels sprouts*, they've gone out of season.'

'I was planning on something bigger,' said Memnos, as the old hollowness moved through him once more. 'A personal statement, perhaps. Possibly rhyming. About love, or death, or going barmy. Something major.'

'Here!' cried his father. 'What about posters for tourists? They're always coming here from the mainland; we could do posters advertising dancing folklorique up the town hall, souvenir shops where they could get them little minotaurs for holding toothpicks, guided tours of the labyrinth. We could go down to the boats and hand 'em round, we'd get ten per cent off the retailers, we could clean up!'

'It's not exactly what I had in mind,' said his son.

His father glared at him.

'Advertising,' he said, 'that's where the money is!'

'Kids!' said his wife. 'Do they listen?'

He sat under a tree. Flies buzzed around his ink. He chewed his twig for the hundredth time. Around him, the parched ground was strewn with crumpled leaves.

He took a fresh one from his bag, smoothed it out, laid it on the board across his knees. Slowly, tongue curling over his upper lip, he wrote:

'It was a dark and stormy night.'

He stopped.

His mind teemed with shapes, people, mountains, ships,

61

jokes, accidents, names, dreams. They floated about, they interleaved, they fragmented.

He tore up the leaf, and plucked another.

'It was the best of times,' he wrote, 'it was the worst of . . .'

'OY!'

Memnos looked up.

Agorophon was galloping down the hill, scattering goats. He fetched up, breathless.

'Journalism!' he gasped.

'What?'

'Nice big leaf, rhubarb, palm, something like that, bring it out every day, nail it up in the town square, stand a couple of big blokes in front of it with clubs, people want to read it, they have to pay! Main news, discus results, drawings of birds with their skirts up, spot-the-javelin contest, seer forecast, classified ads—how about it?'

Memnos shook his head.

'It would be selling out,' he said.

Agorophon clenched his fists.

'At least,' he muttered, 'it'd be selling.'

'That is not,' murmured Memnos, 'what it's all about.'

'It's what some of it's about, mate,' snapped Agorophon.

It took Memnos several years to sail to the mainland, and hardly a night passed on that terrible voyage when he did not regret his decision to leave Crete, nor long for the old companionship of the simple Cretans who had wanted him to abuse his gift.

And when, at last, he arrived, and sat on the pebbled beach, what, he asked himself, had it all been for?

And then he knew.

He had something to write about now.

When the sack of scribbled leaves was full, he strapped it to a mule, and he trekked into Athens, and—

What did one do with a great poem?

He pushed through the hanging beads.

'Is this,' enquired Memnos timidly, 'the registered office of

Homer, Homer, Homer, Homer, Homer, Homer & Homer?'

'Yes,' they said.

'I understand,' said Memnos, putting his sack down, 'that you recite great poetry?'

'Sometimes it's great,' said all the Homers, 'sometimes it's not so great. You win a few, you lose a few. Also, it depends how much you can remember. We take it you know about the oral tradition?'

'It's over,' said Memnos, not without a hint of triumph. 'Mine's written down.'

The Homers looked at one another, sharply.

'*Written down?*'

'It's in two parts. One I called *The Odyssey*. The other I called *The Iliad*.'

'Catchy,' said the Homers. 'Could be very big.'

'Also,' said Memnos, 'I can teach you to read it. Then you could read it aloud everywhere, and I would get rich and famous.'

'So teach,' said the Homers.

And he did.

And when he had gone, the seven Homers split the manuscript up into seven parts, and each Homer learned his seventh by heart.

Then they burned the manuscript.

'Tough on the kid,' said the Homers, 'but business is business.'

This Don For Hire

'Literary scholarship is now a territory occupied or disputed by hard professionals, most often working in academic teams. The days of the free-ranging individual critic, the literary dilettante, the man untied to university departments or Schools of Thought, seem to have gone.'—New York Times

I OPENED THE THIRD DRAWER, left, of my old roll-top desk, the drawer with the gummed label on it that read: PUNCTUATION IN THE LATIN COMEDIES OF ABRAHAM COWLEY, and I moved the dirty manuscript aside and took out the bottle of Cutty Sark, and I poured myself a shot, and I looked at it, and I wondered about when *shot* had come into the language to mean a slug of booze, and since it wasn't in the old beat-up volumes of the OED that stood on the tin shelf behind the desk I thought about writing to John Sykes who would be putting together the S supplement any day now, say by around 1995, just in case there was folding money in it, but then I figured what the hell, he probably has a whole damn OUP team working on the word right now. Computers, teletype, all that.

Then I started wondering about *slug*.

That's the thing with semantics. It can drive you crazy. Some nights I lie awake, smoking and wondering about the deriva-tion of *okay*, watching the neons flashing on and off across the street from my room. I thought about writing to *Notes & Queries* once, they pay up to fifty pee for good paragraphs about *okay*, but then I got side-tracked into thinking about *neon* and how it derived from the Gk, and maybe we ought to change the name, because it wasn't such a new gas any more. Call it *archaion*.

That's the thing with logic. It can drive you crazy. It's all right if you work for one of the big research outfits, ten guys from Harvard putting together a definitive edition of Harrison Ainsworth's letters, a hot trio of Balliol Junior Fellows collaborating on sources and analogues of *Gammer Gurton's Needle*, you have people to talk to, you can delegate, you get fat retainers.

It beats scratching for literary scraps on your own, in a ten-pound-a-week bedsitter on the Iffley Road. I poured another two fingers. I wondered about a short paper on *Drinking Metaphor: Notes Towards A Critical Collation*; if I couldn't interest *Encounter*, there was always *The Licensed Victualler*. Maybe they had an up-market section of readership, college maunciples, say, or *Gawayne* scholars who'd opened nightclubs when the bottom dropped out of Middle English a year or so back.

I put the bottle back in my drawer; a drop of amber stained the title page of my MS, but rapidly absorbed itself without trace in the yellowed paper. It had been around a long time, and stood no chance of publication now, despite the fact that I had taken a whole new line on Cowley's capricious use of the semi-colon: punctuation-wise, *Naufragium Joculare* was a mess, but the world would have to remain ignorant of the truth.

Until, that is, some bunch of Yale hustlers wormed fifty grand out of the Ford Foundation, snatched my idea, and put it out in some coffee-table deal with Harper & Row and NBC, introduced by Alistair Cooke, drawings by Hockney.

I was still staring at the drawer when the door opened and a very expensive smell came in. I looked up.

She was the sort of dame that makes the topless towers of Ilium feel they're on borrowed time.

'It says PRIVAT SCOLAR on the door,' she said huskily. 'It doesn't give a client a lot of confidence.'

'Yeah,' I said, 'I know. It also says I have a Ph.G. You know what good signwriters cost these days?'

'I know what top literary critics cost,' she said. 'That's why I came to you.'

'Gee, thanks,' I said.

'I saw your ad in the TLS,' she said, loosening her tippet so that the fox's face slid off her bust. It had my sympathy. 'I have a problem.'

Sure, I thought, it can't be easy getting through Daddy's allowance when the world was so full of guys stepping on each other to buy you all the jewellery you needed. I didn't say anything, though.

'I'm in my final year at St. Hugh's,' she said. 'I have to get a good degree this summer, or my old man will go bananas. I could lose the Porsche.'

'The quality of mercy,' I quipped, 'you win a few, you . . .'

'What?'

'Forget it,' I said. Kids today, what do they know? 'How can I help?'

'I'm working on Crabbe,' she said.

'That figures,' I said, eyeing her Gucci shoes, her Ken Lane choker. 'Me, I get by on pie and peas from the chippy downstairs. Two nations, like Disraeli said.'

'*George* Crabbe. I opted for this special paper, right? If I do well in that, I thought, it might just help me get by without all this Anglo-Saxon junk, Spenser, Milton. The thing about Crabbe is there isn't much of him, you could read it all up in a couple of days.'

'Who is this you of whom you speak, doll?' I enquired.

'You is this you,' she replied. She opened her purse. 'I have a hundred green ones against a real hot essay delivered this time next week on the subject: *George Crabbe: Last of the Augustans or first of the Romantics?* Here's fifty on account.'

I folded the money.

'Why that particular question?' I asked.

'It's the only one they ever set,' she replied.

The Bodleian Library is a tough place to work. You get your head down, you try to concentrate, but all you hear is these fishnet thighs rasping together. Broads going up to the desks, broads going into the stacks, broads taking a coffee break.

I stuck to it, though. I had my head into *The Village*, and my right hand was filling foolscap faster than a bookie's clerk on Derby Day. Then I felt them come up behind me. I hadn't heard them. No fishnet.

I looked up. They were two of the biggest critics I'd ever seen. Heads like tombstones. One of them leaned across and picked up the book. He dropped it to the floor, and stepped on it.

'Oh, I'm sorry,' he said. 'It looked such a nice book, too.'

66

'It was okay,' I said. 'It did the job.'

'That's what we'd like to talk about,' said the other hood. He put his hand on my shoulder. It was like carrying an iron epaulette.

We stood outside, on the dark staircase.

'We hear you've been asking questions about Crabbe,' said one.

'I have an enquiring mind,' I said.

'Yeah. The thing is, Charlie and I and a couple of other guys from Cornell just happen to be working on Crabbe. We're taking fifteen grand a year each out of Guggenheim. The Fellowship would like to know whether he was the last of the Augustans or the first of the Romantics.'

'What have you found out?' I said.

'Nothing,' said the first.

'We'd like it to stay that way,' said the second. 'It's nice here in Oxford. The river, the au pairs, all that.'

He was standing behind me. I should have known better than to let that happen. I heard the swish as his arm came back.

A black pit opened up, and I fell in.

I walked into Blackwell's bookshop. It's a tense place at the best of times: always a lot of Christ Church muscle about, black belts from Durham, guys with Arts Council grants and lumps in their armpits. They work in teams, you ask for a new book on Spenser's debt to Ariosto, first thing you know you're looking for teeth all over the Children's Section.

I had a lump on my head, and my mouth felt like an emeritus philologist had curled up and died in it, but I went up to the counter anyway, and I asked for everything they had on Crabbe. The girl went pale. I saw her nod, but not whom to.

'I'm sorry,' she said. 'We have no books by or about any person of that name.'

'Come on!' I cried. 'Be serious! *George* Crabbe, last of the Augustans? Or, to put it another way, first of the . . .'

'You heard what the lady said, Mac.'

I turned around, slow. I had to look up a long way. I'd seen the face around, *The Book Programme, Read All About It, Parkinson*; he had a Jap with him. The Jap smiled; he had steel teeth.

'You did that book on Southey,' I said, pleasantly enough. 'Dennis Potter got a fifteen-part serial out of it. You're the Professor of Poetry at . . .'

'This is Doctor Sun,' he said. 'He handles the Japanese end. It leaves him a lot of time for his hobby.'

'What does he do?' I said.

'He breaks things.'

'Blicks,' said Doctor Sun. 'Clitics. You name it.'

'I'm working on Crabbe right now,' said the Professor of Poetry. 'Goodbye.'

I walked out of the bookshop. The fresh air felt good. For about two seconds. That's how long it took for the black sedan to pull away from the kerb. I hurled myself sideways. There were twenty years of scholarship in that hurl.

When I got up again, there was a cop standing beside me. The car was long gone.

'Leavisites,' I said. I dusted my fedora. 'They don't give up easy.'

'I didn't see a thing,' said the cop.

He walked away.

I watched him go. This is a stinking city, I thought. All the rottenness ends up here.

There was nothing left in the Cutty Sark bottle when she came in, but I didn't care. She was in to me for a torn patella, a busted septum, and two bicuspids that had still had a lot of tread left on them; that was enough hospitality for one week.

'Did you do it?' she said.

I threw the big envelope on the desk. She opened it.

'What's this?' she said, after a moment or two.

'It's all you ever need to know about punctuation in the Latin comedies of Abraham Cowley,' I said.

'It isn't what I asked for,' she said.

I smiled. It hurt my face.

'You just described life,' I said. 'Maybe Oxford can still teach a thing or two, after all.'

Saturday Night Fever

'Saturday Night Fever, *which has so far grossed over sixty million dollars, started life as a magazine article entitled "Tribal Rites of a Saturday Night". It is not just a hip treatment of disco culture: this story of a kid who works and sweats all week, living only for his Saturday night explosion, has a whole life inside it.'*—Time Magazine

HE WALKS DOWN THE STREET. Check out that walk! Do those feet touch the concrete?

He walks so light, just the toes touch, the hips have that roll, he walks like a man wearing plimsolls with one heel off. This is because it is Saturday! And Saturday is the day he was going to pick up his brown brogues from the Lightning Shoe Repairs (Estab. 1958) Co. Ltd., only when he hobbled into their reeking premises he could not find the ticket and was shown the notice: Customers Please Produce Ticket And Oblige No Articles Released Without Ticket Yrs Rspctflly The Mgemnt.

He walks so light, because it's Saturday! People in the street go Wow! Thinking: *That guy has a very lousy wooden leg indeed! Either that or he has a real bad boil somewhere, possibly of carbuncle status! Whichever way you slice it, he is not getting the medical attention he deserves!*

They cannot see his heart. His heart is clattering, rim-shots on a snare drum, because it is Saturday, and Saturday is the day he is going to put the shelf up in the garage. He has worked all week, sweated, ground at the numbing routine of writing, editing, trying to park only the circulation manager is in his place, he has lost a lot of good brain cells all week, waiting for Saturday, waiting to get it all together, put the shelf up.

He limps, that snappy limp, into Galway Hardware, Finchley Road. He pauses at the door, sniffing Finchley Road, it is his street, he owns this street, its dreams, its heartaches, its Sainsbury's, its white dotted line going down the middle! It goes on and on, south to Swiss Cottage, north to Henley's Corner, it is all his, his runway, his arena!

'Hi!' snap, snap, go his fingers. 'I need a packet of one-inch Number Eight screws, I need Rawlplugs, I need all that.'

An old lady looks at him. She is from The Neighbourhood. She is Real People.

'I was first,' she screams.

'Some people can't see a bleeding queue when it's staring them in the wossname!' cries a woman in a hairnet, waving a jeroboam of Sanilav.

He loves them! They are Life!

'I'm sorry,' he says, because he loves them.

'Never mind sorry,' shrieks the old lady, 'sorry won't get my bathplug bought!'

'Was that with or without the chain?' says the ironmonger. Check that style! Check that mongering! This is *uno chi capisce*, this is one who knows.

There is a lot of neighbourhood blah after this, it is a very demotic scene, the people talk about lengths of bath-chain, about plug-diameters, the hairnet with the Sanilav tells about the time she nearly bought the wrong-sized washer for a tap that wouldn't stop dripping, an old guy examining rat-poisons in a corner chips in about how if the plug was too big it wouldn't fit in the hole, but the old lady comes right back at him and snaps that if it's too small then there's no way the water is going to stay in the bath, the ironmonger disappears into the back of the shop, it's a wonderful rich canvas, the guy in the one-and-a-half plimsolls hops from one foot to the other, does he scream, does he bang his head on the wall, does he pick up a hoe and kebab the Neighbourhood People? No! Because it's Saturday, it's the day he's waited the whole week for, it's *his* day!

He just chokes a little, bites through his lower lip, pushes his fist through his trouser pocket. His whole body is *vibrant*.

He limps out of Galway hardware, screwless, into his street. The climate has changed, but it is his rain, he *owns* this rain, it is coming up through the ex-heel of *his* plimsoll! Hell, like who needs garage-shelves anyhow, it's only somewhere to stand the emulsion he was going to paint the ceiling with, and as he kicked over the emulsion that morning as the result of its standing on the floor of the garage instead of on the shelf he hasn't put up yet, what does it matter?

He looks at his partially eau-de-nil trousers. They have a very pleasing effect, in the right light. Even the partially eau-de-nil wing of his car looks pretty good, if you park the car so's you can't see the partially eau-de-nil wing.

He takes out his shopping list, unfolds it, snap, snap, the rain comes down, plop, plop, the list reads: 3 lb flggge, 6 jlllbbb, 4 large schlg, the rest of the list runs off the page as he watches, a week's provisions dissolve on his cuff.

He lopes back ten blocks to his partially eau-de-nil car, a really awesome lope on account of capillary attraction is drawing most of the climate up the sock in the heelless plimsoll, he is drowning from the ground up. Back at his car there is a parking ticket, Saturday is the day he gets parking tickets, his whole body *reacts* to the parking ticket, he drives back to his house, it is easily recognisable due to where none of the other houses in the street have eau-de-nil plimsoll-prints all over the front path.

And still only noon! Still twelve hours of Saturday to go, all his, throbbing!

His woman is there. She looks at him. He looks at her. You can feel the charge. It goes back a long way, this electricity: man, woman, perhaps it goes back as long a way as it is possible to go.

She says: 'Did you get the courgettes?'

He says: 'So that's what they were!'

She says: 'Did you get the four large aubergines?'

He says: 'Ah. Four large aubergines.'

A huskiness creeps into her voice, his lithe shoulders do wild things, shrug, shrug, their conversation rises and falls, they are really communicating, no outsider could guess what is passing between them, only these two know it is about freaky things like why there are eau-de-nil footprints all over the hall carpet or the problems of making aubergine, courgette and mortadella quiche when you do not have any aubergines, courgettes, mortadella or Jus-Rol pastry.

It ends the only way such things can end when man and woman breathe such passion into one another: he takes off his plimsolls and his liquescent socks and slops out of the kitchen.

He is terrifically cool, incredibly laid back: he gets through the whole of lunch with everybody staring at him. The children do not stare at him the whole time; some of the time they stare at their cold lunch. His daughter contrives to stare at both simultaneously, getting down to table level and coming at him over the rim of her untouched plate, like Mister Chad.

He is thinking: *Saturday! It is all worth it for Saturday!*

After lunch, he rolls out to the garden on the balls of his feet, a fascinating gait he has developed as the result of having pieces of Lego dropped into his Wellingtons; he is like some kind of wild animal. Out here, it is *his* garden. That is *his* fence, lying flat on *his* budding peonies; the decapitated buds roll in the windy wet, withered as prunes.

'Yes, that is *your* fence,' confirms another Neighbourhood Person, looking through the gap.

'I thought it was joint-owned,' ripostes the guy, snap, snap, cool as ever.

'No, that's where you're wrong.'

'Oh.'

The neighbour's beagle barrels through the gap and pees on the last intact peony. The neighbour goes back in his house. The dog follows.

Everything in the greenhouse is dead. That frost. Saturday is the day for going to the greenhouse and wondering if the geraniums are still dead.

If anything, they are deader than they were last week.

He looks up at the greenhouse roof, or where it was before the children learned cricket. Through the holes, on a good Saturday, you can see God.

There is nothing he can do in the garden. He could maybe make a shelf for the garage out of the fallen fence, if only he had some screws, some Rawlplugs.

If he had more paint, he could maybe paint the whole car eau-de-nil.

He goes back into the house. It is Saturday, Wales are playing France; except on his television set. This is tuned to a channel where cowboys are playing Indians. He thinks about a sudden dash to the tuning knobs, but a lot of children are staring at him, malevolent from non-lunch, daring him to cross them again.

He goes out of the room with that terrific stylish shuffle, like a man carrying a bathful of rocks on his neck. The light is beginning to fade. *Check out that light!* Saturday is slipping away!

He keeps the *Radio Times* in his lavatory, so the children will not reconstitute it as glove puppets. He leafs through it with Saturday Night eagerness. Soon, zip, zip, it will be time for the fourth repeat of *M*A*S*H*, for *Saturday Night at the Mill*, for a *Lively Arts* interview with William Walton's auntie's butcher, for news of Lebanon, starring cheery Peter Woods. For tomorrow's weather with Michael Fish, or tomorrow's fish with Michael Weather.

He puts a foot on the stair. The foot is numb. Could be pneumonia, pleurisy, gangrene, any one of a hundred really terrific stylish things.

She says: 'Where are you going?'

He says: 'I am going up to the attic to write an article. Sometimes an article can end up grossing over sixty million dollars.'

She says: 'Ha, ha.'

He says: 'I feel like working.'

She says: 'But it's *Saturday!*'

The Idiot

'Examination fever is a summer disease that in the Soviet Union is caught not merely by pupils. The worst cases are among parents. Soviet parents are as ambitious as parents anywhere for their children's success, and a degree or diploma is still a passport to financial and social advancement in Russia. Parents who fear their children may not do well have been known to pull every string they can.—The Times

ON A PUNISHINGLY HOT morning towards the end of June 197–, a short, harrassed, dishevelled figure could be seen scurrying along S— Street, in the small industrial town of P. Despite the abrasive heat, he wore a long, tattered herringbone overcoat and a heavy fur hat that had seen better days.

In his two arms he bore a huge object that had been amateurishly wrapped in second-hand cartridge paper and tied with different sorts of string. The package was almost as big as the man, but he hurried on, looking neither to right nor left, clearly hoping that nobody would notice him or his extraordinary burden.

That this deception was not entirely successful could be judged from the cries that followed in his disordered wake.

'Oh, you have knocked me down with your enormous parcel, Nikolai Nikolayevich!'

And

'See, appalling Nikolai Nikolayevich, what havoc your passage has wrought upon my wheeled basket!'

And

'I curse you for a rogue and a scoundrel, Nikolai Nikolayevich, who has affrighted my beloved little dog with his vile mountain of cardboard!'

Nikolai Nikolayevich (for it was indeed he) paid no attention, however, to the bitter shrieks of his fellow citizens. He hurried on, and did not stop until he came to the doorway of a tall grey apartment block at the corner of S— Street and G— Road, just before V— Avenue, to be precise, where he turned inside.

In the dark narrow corridor which smelt of cabbage and cats and overrated nineteenth-century novels, Nikolai Nikolayevich stopped, wedged by his enormous bundle against the nicotine-coloured lincrusta of the ancient wall. As he struggled to free himself, doors opened along the vile passage, and voices cried out.

'Is that you, disgusting Nikolai Nikolayevich, who is ruining the communal dado?'

And

'We hold you responsible, Nikolai Nikolayevich, for all damage incurred to the linoleum!'

And

'Oh, that I had my youth once more, I should kick that accursed Nikolai Nikolayevich until his shins bled!'

At last, the hapless Nikolai Nikolayevich succeeded in freeing his giant parcel and himself; and, gaining the worn wooden staircase, he struggled up to the —teenth floor.

His wife, when she opened the door of their tiny apartment, clasped her reddened hands and wailed for a time, as she did every day. Nikolai Nikolayevich waited with his customary fortitude until she had finished. It was, after all, the one entertainment she could afford on his miserable salary.

When it was over, she helped him carry in his parcel and stand it in the hall. So small was the flat that half the parcel poked into their living-room, where their son sat at a rude table, staring out of the window. He did not turn.

'See what your wonderful father Nikolai Nikolayevich has brought you, little Boris!' cried his mother.

The boy looked round, with dead eyes.

'What is it?' he said.

'It is a bicycle, little Boris!' cried his father. 'Nearly new, with a one-speed gear, and most of a bell. It is for when you pass your examinations to go to the grammar school.'

'But suppose I do not pass my examinations?' said little Boris.

At this, his mother threw herself prostrate upon the pitiful bare boards and shrieked so loud that their one reproduction ikon fell off its pin.

The colour drained from his father's stair-empurpled face.

'*Not pass?*' he croaked. 'Not go to the grammar school and become qualified and wear a homburg hat and receive a monthly salary, so that people will point at you in the street and cry: *That is Boris, son of Nikolai Nikolayevich, in the homburg hat, carrying a buff envelope with his monthly salary in*, is that what you want?'

'The bicycle is a bribe,' said little Boris, his voice like stone. 'It is a deviationist trick, designed to make me forget the wonderful egalitarian principles by which all truly loyal Soviet citizens must live. While we are on the subject, how did you come by it?'

'It fell off a tractor,' muttered his father.

'TELL HIM, Nikolai Nikolayevich!' screamed his wife. 'Tell him that you pawned your genuine tin watch to purchase it!'

'Is it true?' snapped little Boris.

Nikolai Nikolayevich nodded glumly.

'Buying, selling, pawning, trading,' and here the boy shook his head grimly, 'this is a bad business, Nikolai Nikolayevich my father.'

The three might have stayed thus staring wretchedly at one another for some weeks, had at that moment the doorbell not sounded. Nikolai Nikolayevich took the two steps necessary to reach the door, and opened it.

'Oh, oh, oh, it is Pedagogue Dobrinin, schoolmaster to our beloved little Boris!' he exclaimed. 'I must fall and kiss the hem of your beautifully tailored overcoat!'

'Get up, esteemed Nikolai Nikolayevich,' replied the academic with becoming gravity. 'I believe I heard something clunk as you hit the floor, and I should not like to think of anything breaking, nudge, nudge, wink, wink, eh?'

Nikolai Nikolayevich struggled to his feet, snatching at his wispy forelock.

'Quite so, master, quite so,' he muttered. And here he opened his own shabby coat to reveal the reason why he thus wore it in the heat of summer.

The schoolmaster looked at the bottles.

'This is, I trust, the genuine article, Nikolai Nikolayevich, born 1820 and still going strong? It will not stand well with little Boris if I discover these bottles to contain only cold tea laced with a touch of wolf-piddle to deceive the inexperienced palate.'

Nikolai Nikolayevich gasped!

'That is the very best, Pedagogue Dobrinin!' he cried. 'It was sold to the personal friend of a personal friend by the British Ambassador, who is having a hard time making ends meet these days.'

'As are we all, Nikolai Nikolayevich,' countered the schoolmaster. 'Foreign cigarettes, to take a random example, are impossibly expensive, are they not?'

'Curse me for a forgetful fool!' howled Nikolai Nikolayevich, whipping off his old fur hat.

'Why,' exclaimed the schoolmaster, 'you have a carton of Lucky Strike on your head, Nikolai Nikolayevich!'

'Take them!' shouted that worthy man. 'Smoke them in good health, Pedagogue Dobrinin!'

After the schoolmaster had been bowed out, little Boris sat scribbling in his notebook for some minutes.

His parents beamed!

What joy for us, dear Reader, had we been there to witness the twin delights of parental devotion and filial obedience!

Little Boris was still scribbling and his parents were still beaming when the doorbell rang yet again. Nikolai Nikolayevich threw the door wide; and immediately fell back into the tiny apartment, his forehead all but touching the floor!

'Examiner Rosnetsov!' mumbled his trembling lips, 'Examiner Rosnetsov! See, wife, it is Examiner Rosnetsov himself who graces our unworthy hovel with his august magnificence, his light-weight suit, his silk tie, his astounding totally leather shoes!'

Examiner Rosnetsov strode into the room. His rimless glasses flashed the cold fire of authority, but they did not turn to little Boris. He put his sponge-bag down upon the table.

'Is this the woman?' barked Examiner Rosnetsov.

'This is she, sir,' replied Nikolai Nikolayevich.

'She is somewhat older than I had been led to believe,' said the great official. 'Also, she is bandy.'

'A trick of the light, no more!' cried Nikolai Nikolayevich. 'Would I, worm that I am, dare to deceive so eminent an educational paragon as Examiner Rosnetsov?'

'It is, however, a not entirely unattractive bandiness.'

'Ah. Now I look again,' said Nikolai Nikolayevich, 'it is just possible the knees of my lovely wife do not touch. It is doubtless the result of carrying the weight of her magnificent bosom. And are her hips not as I described them in my letter?'

'I have seen worse,' replied Examiner Rosnetsov. 'You may leave us now.'

'Thank you, Examiner Rosnetsov!' cried Nikolai Nikolayevich gratefully. 'Come, little Boris, your great examiner and your dear mother wish to be alone.'

Little Boris rose from the table at last, still scribbling. He pocketed his notebook. He walked out, behind his father, and followed him down the echoing stairs.

Out in the hot street, little Boris expressed his desire to go off on his own, down to the river to think.

'The boy is an intellectual!' cried his father, watching him go. 'The boy shall one day have a diploma, a Zim convertible, a private lavatory!'

Little Boris turned the corner, out of his father's sight. But he did not go down to the river. He quickened his pace, towards a public telephone.

After the two KGB men had dragged the screaming Nikolai Nikolayevich and his wailing wife out of the apartment and down the stairs, their inspector put his arm around the thin shoulders of little Boris.

'You did very well, little Boris,' he said. 'These evil people have engaged in every conceivable form of deviation, corruption and perversion for which our glorious state makes statutory provision. Mother Russia will throw the key away! And she will undoubtedly see to it that such loyalty and selflessness as yours do not go unrecognised. Of that you may be sure! Tell me, little Boris, what shall be your reward?'

Little Boris looked up into the granite face.

'I should like a place at grammar school,' he said.

Man's Estate

IN the beginning, God acquired the heaven and the earth.

2 And the earth was without form, and void, and represented a wonderful opportunity for the imaginative developer; and darkness was upon the face of the deep, but scheduled for major structural alteration at an early date.

3 And God said, Let there be light: and the darkness was tastefully converted at the developer's own expense.

4 And God made the light the subject of his personal inspection, that it was good: and God divided the light from the darkness, to the highest specifications.

5 And God called the light Day, and the darkness he called Night. And the evening (which was within a stone's throw of the Night) and the morning (which was most convenient for easy reach of the Day) together constituted a virtually fully detached unit.

6 And God granted outline planning permission for a prestige firmament in the midst of the waters, so that the entire project would enjoy full waterside frontage.

7 And God erected the firmament: and to underline the extremely high quality designed to appeal to the most discriminating taste in homes, he called it Heaven.

8 And God said, Let the waters under Heaven be gathered together unto one place, to constitute a substantial area for recreation, yet one with considerable industrial potential for the discerning businessman seeking to diversify; and let the dry land appear. And it was so.

9 And God called the dry land Earth; and the gathering together of the waters called he Seas: and at those points where the Seas lapped against the Earth, he called it nothing to worry about.

10 And God said, Let the

earth bring forth attractive lawns needing a minimum of attention, and borders offering a wealth of mature flowering shrubs, and numerous climbing plants including clematis, wisteria and a veritable riot of honeysuckle, plus good-size plots for the keen vegetable enthusiast.

11 And it was so.

12 And God said, Let there be carriage drives.

13 And God saw that not all of the earth faced South; and where it faced South, called he it South-facing; and where it faced East, called he it partly South-facing; and where it faced West, called he it largely South-facing; and where it faced North, called he it Enjoying - broad - outlook - all - round.

14 And when God looked upon his work, and the countless delightful plots, and the countless charming plots, and the countless convenient plots, and the countless exclusive plots, and the countless substantial plots, and the countless spacious plots, and the countless prime plots, and the countless quality plots, and the countless valuable plots, and the countless enviable plots, and the countless ideal plots, and the even more countless unique plots, all of which were just in the market, he found them good.

15 And God said, Let us make man in our image, after our likeness, quietly traditional and yet containing the ultimate in modern features; and let him have dominion over all the plots on earth.

16 So God created man in his own image; male and female created he them, similar in basic design but differing in details according to individual taste.

17 And God planted a lovely, but manageable, garden eastward (though South-facing) in Eden; and there he put the man whom he had formed.

18 And out of the ground made the LORD God to grow every tree that is pleasant for the sight, and good for food, including a very old apricot which could be counted on to produce at least two or three fruit a year and looked truly fabulous against the wall down by the ample parking space for up to three vehicles.

19 And a river went out of Eden to water the garden; which also represented an attractive investment, since fishing rights went with the

property. There was also more than enough space for a swimming-pool, if required, plus a hard tennis court, the whole extending to some two-and-a-ninth acres to form a truly delightful self-contained leisure area.

20 And the LORD God took the man, and put him into the garden of Eden to dress it and to keep it; and to build thereon a detached residence in keeping with the truly salubrious environment, after the nature of the planning permission, and to hold it against a 999-year lease, at a peppercorn rent.

21 And the man, who was called Adam, enquired in his wise as to whether the freehold was available for purchase; and there was thunder about that place for a goodly time.

22 And Adam erected himself an executive property of distinction in a much sought after position overlooking a favoured reach of the Eden, completely secluded, yet within five minutes walk of all the beasts of the field and all the fowls of the air.

23 He split the level, so that the dining recess was three gracious steps up from the elegant lounge, the two combining to form a truly impressive entertainments area. It would have suited a diplomat, or film person.

24 He installed a dream kitchen; it had countless fabulous features.

25 And above, reached by a staircase that was a feature of the property, built he a magnificent bedroom, fully fitted; and, en-suite, a bathroom. And there yet remained ample space.

26 And God saw the residence; and saw that it was exclusive. And he noted the ample space above, more than enough for two more bedrooms plus lavish space for storage, or maid.

27 And the LORD God said, It is not good that the man should be alone; I will make him an help meet for him. And he caused a deep sleep to fall upon Adam, and he slept: and he took one of his ribs, and closed up the flesh instead thereof, and made good.

28 And the rib, which the LORD God had taken from the man, made he a woman, despite being up to here with work; and brought her to the man.

29 And the man took her into the house; and said, In celebration I shall call this attractive residence Adeve.

30 And the woman said, Evam.

31 And the woman looked about her; and said, It may be executive to you, but it is not executive to me. And she caused the man to build an extension in cedarwood upon that which had been built before, and she caused him to convert the loft space into a play area. And above the extension, there was erected a granny flat.

32 And God came to Adam, and waxed exceeding wrath, and said, What is that wooden thing stuck on the delightful brick elevations to side and rear? And what is that thing on top of it?

33 And Adam replied in this wise: the thing is a room extension, a charming suntrap throughout the year, and the thing on top of it is a granny flat.

34 And God said, A *granny* flat?

35 And Adam thought awhile.

36 And replied, All right, then, how about a sauna?

37 And the LORD God waxed terrible in his fury. And he said, Hast thou ignored the planning permission? Hast thou flouted all the requirements and stipulations of the lease that I granted unto you?

38 And the man said, The woman whom thou gavest to be with me, she has persuaded me to this.

39 And God said unto the woman, What is this that thou hast done?

40 And the woman replied, The property was ripe for extension, there was no point staying stuck in two rooms with all that space going begging, I wanted somewhere with a bit of tone. Didn't I?

41 And God said, I will greatly multiply thy sorrow and thy conception; in sorrow thou shalt bring forth children. They shall fill those rooms that thou has built, contrary to mine of the 15th ultimo; they shall write on the walls, and break the windows, and get their heads caught in the banisters, and scream. They shall block the plugs and the drains, they shall knock the tiles from the roof, they shall pull up the shrubs and make waste the velvet lawns. They shall kick the skirtings to pieces.

42 And Adam cried, Before we know it, this will be a property in need of some minor decoration, despite being basically sound.

43 And God looked about him, and saw that the

situation and the dwelling were indeed second to none; and that a substantial price could be expected for the freehold.

44 Therefore the LORD God sent them forth from the garden of Eden. He drove out the man; and he placed at the east of the garden Cherubims, and a flaming sword which turned every way; and the approach to the house alone made it worth easily six figures.

It's Mad Masters, My World!

'*1945. The Führer takes a very hopeful view of the situation. Stalin may take an about-turn in war policy . . . we could then both pursue the struggle against England.*'—Josef Goebbels Diary, from The Observer.

'*The new study concludes that the CIA, the FBI and the KGB all covered up over Lee Harvey Oswald's life as a defector living in Russia.*'—The Guardian

'*Nixon told me that he wanted his opponents to think he was mad. "I call it the Madman Theory, Bob. I want the North Vietnamese to believe I will do anything".*'—H. R. Haldeman, quoted in the Daily Mail.

'*Was Russia prepared to join with America in a war against China?*'—Daily Telegraph.

From the Diaries of Lee Harvey Goebbels

March 18 1945

I AM in the Führerbunker nursery dismembering my Action Pole when H. R. Himmler enters. He glares at my old man, and it is clear to all and sundry where he is pretty hacked off about something.

'Look here, Goebbels,' he says, 'I just heard where we are too late to screw the 1945 election!'

My old man is crestfallen. He is also crazy as a flea, but this is not immediately apparent, especially as most of the grown-ups in the room have wires on their heads, write dirty letters to Dinah Shore, believe themselves to be cans of beans, sleep on top of the pelmets, and generally carry on in a manner likely to unsettle the average taxpayer.

It it, however, what makes them great leaders.

'What's an election, Vater?' enquires Richard Milhous Eichmann, a gangling boy, looking up from his laboratory bench. A brilliant biologist, he is attempting to mate a parrot with a rat as part of his scheme to manufacture a personal assistant.

'We plan to do this deal with the Americans,' explains his father. 'If we can get them to enter a bilateral treaty with us to join arms against the Russians, we have promised to hold free elections in a rehabilitated Germany. The Campaign To Re-Elect The Führer has therefore been working on plans to break into the HQ of the Opposition, whoever they are, soon after the Armistice.'

'Will the Americans buy the pact, Vater?'

'That depends on how crazy Roosevelt is. The CIA tell us he's pretty crazy, but is he crazy enough is the big question.'

'That is all academic as of this moment in time,' mutters H. R. Himmler. 'We have blown our credibility.'

'You mean,' says my old man, 'that the NKVD has discovered that Goering is a fag and is going to use the information to discredit us in the Schwarzwald primary? I knew they would. He has J. Edgar Goering embroidered on his suspender-belts. He leaves them everywhere. It was only a matter of time.'

Himmler shakes his head.

'Worse,' he says, 'the Russians are entering Berlin!'

'Ridiculous!' screams my old man. 'I understood you had engineered a pact between us and Russia to declare war on Britain?'

'Stalin wouldn't buy it,' replies Himmler. 'He figures that by taking Berlin he will in a much better position to wipe out his present allies.'

'Wow und Himmel!' exclaims J. Enoch Doenitz Jr. 'You have to hand it to Uncle Joe, men. That is craziness of a truly visionary order. No wonder they are wiping the floor with us.'

'Not so fast,' replies Eichmann's dad, 'we have one or two crazy tricks left up our sleeves. It looks to me like the only way we can make Germany great again is by getting beaten. Our people in the FBI have been sending us stuff on this George Marshall. From first indications, he is a madman's madman.'

'How do we get beaten before it's too late?' enquires Doenitz.

Eichmann looks round, slow.

'We have to assassinate the Führer,' he whispers.

There is a long pause. Finally, everyone looks at me. I am small, but I am wiry, and besides I have this really terrific mail-order rifle.

June 30 1950

The fifth anniversary of my arrival in the United States, entitling me to citizenship. It was a great idea of my old man's having me emigrate, on account of he saw where the post-war German government would be filled with crazy Nazis by the crazy Allied leadership to counter the crazy Bolshevik threat, and there would not be openings for a bright kid for maybe a generation or more.

'Go west, young man!' he shrieked at me, just before poisoning himself, crowning a great career with true manic genius.

He was right. Many of us felt that Harry S. Truman was not crazy enough to last, but my old man knew the signs. Within six months of taking office, Harry had A-bombed the Japs into becoming powerful allies, and now less than three years later, here we are in another major war. The Korean operation promises to be the kind of fiasco that could lead to a South-East Asian policy as crazy as anything the world has ever seen. I understand from R. M. Eichmann, who has changed his name and gone into American politics with the aid of a KGB scholarship, that the Russians are so thrown by Truman's craziness they are keeping out of Korea altogether. It is increasingly apparent that Stalin is becoming prematurely sane. Is Russia finished?

October 30 1956

No, it isn't. Today, the Russian tanks entered Budapest to flatten the people's democracy and make it safe for the people's democracy. This Nikita Khrushchev is clearly as crazy as they come, which is why no one will try to stop him. It's true Eisenhower is slightly crazy, but it tends to express itself in golf, which does not frighten anyone.

How crazy is Anthony Eden? He has invaded Egypt, which is a good sign for Western democracy, especially as the French, who have been encouragingly crazy over Algeria, are backing him up, but medical opinion here is that he is less crazy than Nasser and will probably recover after a few days and pull out. The pity is that Eisenhower is not crazy enough (*see above*) to get involved, which means World War III is not on the cards.

R. M. ex-Eichmann comes to see me this evening. He spent some years working with Joe McCarthy, and looks to be shaping up pretty crazy; he is now Eisenhower's VP, and suggests I assassinate him, but the KGB is against this on the grounds that the Veep is nowhere near crazy enough yet to be considered a world leader. They feel that Krushchev would roll right over him, and world domination could put millions of KGB agents out of jobs, especially the millions that are in the CIA and the FBI and have swimming pools and Lincoln convertibles.

Life is therefore dull. Eden is replaced, so I do not even get the chance to take a shot at him. True, Hitler's son writes me regularly, but he is only looking for publishers.

October 18 1961

A wonderful opportunity missed! I knew I should not have left America after the Bay of Pigs showed just how crazy Kennedy was, and now he has locked horns with Krushchev who is banging his shoes on tables and generally coming on real loco, and where am I? I am in Paris, shooting at de Gaulle whenever he sticks his head out. No question but that he is mad as a hatter, but he is not major league compared with Kennedy, who is squaring up to Nikita in the Caribbean like there was no tomorrow, as there very probably isn't. Also Kennedy has expanded the war in Vietnam on the grounds that it is the only way to stop it. I am in two minds: he is so crazy I could kiss his feet, on the other hand he cannot last.

November 30 1963

Wasn't I right?

I see the KGB has pinned the rap on Oswald. All very well, but there is now a considerable craziness gap, unless Johnson manages to expand the war.

July 1 1964

Johnson manages to expand the war. He explains he is doing this to bring the war to an end. He could last for a thousand years. He is also selling arms to both sides in the Middle East in a last-minute bid for peace in the area. Not unnaturally, Khrushchev is on the wane; his craziness, in the face of Vietnam, is no match for the Americans. The CIA attempt to interest him in a pact between Russia and China to declare war on the United States so that they can go in and undermine South America while world attention is elsewhere, but he does not buy it.

October 3 1964

Khrushchev discredited. This Brezhnev is an unknown quantity, although his immediate instruction to step up the MIRV missile system, which will increase nuclear overkill to the point where everyone gets killed sixteen times instead of just seven, is very heartening.

June 18 1968

Johnson halts the bombing of North Vietnam and announces his retirement. The two events go, naturally, hand-in-hand; having shown that, deep down, he wasn't crazy all along, he has no future.

Unlike Brezhnev, who is really blossoming! In August, he crushes Czechoslovakia to save it from tyranny.

In November, R. M. ex-Eichmann is elected President. It is possible he is the craziest person to hold major office since our great Führer. He tells Haldeman, I discover from our KGB man in M15, that he actually *wants* everyone to think he's crazy. There is only one person crazier than a crazy person and that is a person who wants everyone to *think* he is a crazy person. It is called Catch-23. It is the best catch there is.

He could become so great, I will have to assassinate him. It is that kind of world.

August 12 1974

He's gone. All that stuff he heard in the bunker, it finally got through to him. But a great act of craziness to go out on, you have to admit it. My old man would've been proud.

Gerald Ford is not crazy, unfortunately. He is dumb, which is very different. You don't scare anybody, except maybe your family.

We may have to look elsewhere for great leaders. I hear a lot of talk about Amin, Gaddafi, Bhutto, Smith, Arafat, Mintoff, Vorster, it could be the great powers are a spent force, we could be looking at a whole new order if some of these guys get the breaks.

The CIA, the FBI, the KGB, are everywhere working on it. They say there's a good chance Mrs Gandhi can make a bomb. Also, everybody in China is going crazy. Madam Mao recently approached the Sweeney with a view to getting them to mediate in a non-aggression pact with Sardinia.

Word is, she intends to attack Cannes from the south.

November 25 1976

Goodbye, Ford!

This new man talks directly to God. I think we could well be on a winner.

A Little Leaning

'*The pub should become a major centre of further education, TUC chief Len Murray told an Open University conference yesterday. Education should begin where people gathered together.*'—Daily Mail

THE MAN IN THE HERRINGBONE overcoat raised his Guinness.

'Drink deep,' he cried, 'or taste not the Peruvian spring!'

He drank. They all did.

'Alexandra Pipe,' said the man in the herringbone overcoat.

'Who?' enquired the man in the Orient scarf.

'Only one of our greatest poets,' snapped the man in the herringbone overcoat. He fixed the man in the Orient scarf with a ballbearing eye. 'Or poetess,' he said, 'if you want to be pedantous.'

The man in the Orient scarf said nothing.

'What does it mean?' asked the man in the Wimpey jacket.

The herringbone overcoat looked at him, pityingly.

'It is one of the most famous couplings in the language, you ignorant nurd,' he said. 'A little leaning is a dangerous thing/Drink deep, or taste not the Peruvian spring!'

They thought about this for a while, nodding respectfully.

'That Tower of Pizza,' said the Orient scarf, finally. 'There's a thing.'

'You're right there,' said the Wimpey jacket. 'I wouldn't like to have been on that job. There was people dropping cannon-balls off.'

'Garibaldi,' said the herringbone overcoat firmly. 'And it was apples. They was testing for gravity. Garibaldi had this tower built so's he could drop apples off and see if there was any gravity about. It's where we get *eureka* from.'

'What is?' said the Orient scarf.

90

'Stone me, don't you know bleeding nothing?' cried the herringbone overcoat. '*Eureka* is Italian for gravity. Every time one of his apples hit the ground, they all shouted out.'

'I thought he invented the biscuit,' said the Orient scarf.

The herringbone overcoat banged down his empty glass on the marble table-top. A number of customers looked round. A man at the next table leaned across.

'Do you mind?' he said sharply. 'There's people over here trying to discuss the Second Law of Wossname.'

'Oh, pardonnez-moi!' replied the herringbone overcoat, heavily. 'I assumed all the scientists was in the public.'

In the blotched temple of the man at the next table, a small vein began to writhe like a lugworm.

'One of these days,' he said, 'your whole bleeding faculty is going to find itself looking for teeth all over the car-park.'

He turned back to his seminar, who were painstakingly constructing a molecular chain out of crisps.

'Physicists!' snorted the herringbone overcoat to his class. 'I wouldn't send 'em out to post a letter. Where was I?'

'Garibaldi,' said the Orient scarf obstinately, 'and his biscuits.'

'Yes,' said the herringbone overcoat. 'Answer me one thing: did I *say* he never invented the biscuit? He didn't spend all his time dropping apples off things, you know. In them days there was no such thing as specialisation; people used to do everything. It was called the Resemblance.'

'Why was it called that?' said the Wimpey jacket.

'Werl, because everything resembled everything else, I shouldn't wonder. No job too large or small, as it were. Take Leonardo D. Finchley, he'd run you up a bicycle in the morning, you'd come in dinner-time to collect it and he'd knock off your portrait while you was stood at the till. Afternoons, he used to go out sculpting. Amazing, for a Wop.'

The Wimpey jacket, whose forehead had been growing more and more furrowed, suddenly brightened.

'I don't fancy their chances in Argentina, mind,' he said. 'If it was up to me, I'd drop Bettega back to midfield and put——'

The herringbone overcoat withered him silent.

''Course,' he said, 'the English was no slouches when it come to the Resemblance. Take Sir Sidney Phillips, poet, soldier, critic——'

'Clarinettist,' said the Orient scarf.

'What?' snapped the herringbone overcoat.

'And bandleader,' said the Orient scarf. 'We got his *Canadian Capers* up home. With *Sweet Georgia Brown* on the flip side.'

The herringbone overcoat chewed his lip for a moment.

'Yes, werl,' he muttered, 'that just bears it out. Anything they cared to turn their hands to. He had his head chopped off by Queen Elizabeth of course, so it wasn't all beer and skittles.'

'No!' cried the Wimpey jacket. 'Recently?'

'Queen Elizabeth the *First*,' sighed the herringbone overcoat.

'Ah. Werl, he was no Acker Bilk,' said the Orient scarf. 'Even so, killing him's coming it a bit strong. Wonder why she bothered knighting him in the first place, if she didn't like clarinets?'

'Because,' cried the herringbone overcoat, leaning forward and poking the Orient scarf in the chest with a thick forefinger, 'he only come back from America with fags and chips, didn't he?'

'Gerroff!'

'Straight up. Yes, he was probably the best friend the working man ever had. Which reminds me, who's getting them in?'

The Orient scarf rose reluctantly, and went off to the bar. The herringbone overcoat scowled after him.

'Always chipping in,' he muttered, 'always got sunnink to say for himself, hasn't he? And he's pig-ignorant. There's none so dumb as them who won't be taught. I'm seriously thinking of washing my hands of him. Far as I'm concerned, he can go and do bloody geology with them poufs in the snug.'

The Orient scarf returned with the glasses.

'Flora Robson,' he said.

'What?'

'She was doing Queen Elizabeth a couple of Sundays back. On the box. And I'll tell you one thing, there was no mention of Sid Phillips. *And* it was someone else brought the fags back.'

'Sid Phillips was probably dead by then,' murmured the Wimpey jacket tactfully.

The herringbone overcoat ignored him.

'*Flora Robson?*' he shouted. 'Stone me, I don't think I've ever come across anyone as dumb in all my years of teaching! Flora Robson, sonny boy, was as black as the ace of wossname! Flora Robson, may I remind you, was the one who sang *Old Man River* in *Gone With the Wind*! And whatever else Queen Elizabeth may have been, she wasn't a nig-nog!'

The Orient scarf glowered at him sullenly.

'Next thing,' ranted the herringbone overcoat, purpling, 'next thing, you'll tell me I don't know nothing about people of the coon persuasion! Ten years working with 'em up the depot. I prob'ly know more about the Indian Mutiny than Buffalo bloody Bill himself!'

'Indian Mutiny?' enquired the Wimpey jacket, desperate to change the subject, partly because the thermodynamicists at the next table were now, as the result of the noise, beginning to wrap their belts around their fists.

The herringbone overcoat softened at his prize student's question.

'Captain Blight,' he explained. 'He cast all these blackies adrift in an open boat and they went off to the Pitcairn Islands and gave everybody VD.'

'No!' exclaimed the Wimpey jacket.

'It's in all the books,' confirmed the herringbone overcoat. 'Hardly surprising there's a swing to the Conservatives, is there? You wouldn't catch me dead in one of them Tandoori restaurants, I can tell you!'

'Bloody hell,' said the Wimpey jacket, paling. 'We had one of them Vesta curries Tuesday.'

'Yes, werl, that's what history's all about, isn't it?' The herringbone overcoat tapped the table with his matchbox. 'Those who refuse to learn from their mistakes are doomed to repeat them.'

'That's good,' said the Orient scarf, 'who said it?'

The herringbone overcoat looked at him, hard.

'I did,' he said. 'Don't you ever listen to nothing?'

The Orient scarf did not reply.

'It's a wonderful thing, education,' said the Wimpey jacket.

Domestic Drama

The court case involving John Osborne and the domestic couple he sacked for inefficiency has of course had immense repercussions throughout the sensitive world of the theatre.

Dramatis Personae

SNOUT	*Ex-caretaker to Mr Harold Pinter*
ANTONIO ⎫ IGNACIA ⎭	*Ex-couple to Mr Tom Stoppard*
SADIE	*Ex-cook to Mr Arnold Wesker*
FIFI	*Ex-au pair to Mr Brian Rix*
HODGE	*Ex-butler to Mr Alan Ayckbourn*
MRS GLAND	*Ex-governess to Mr Paul Raymond*
SPOT DOUGLAS-HOME	*A dog*

The action takes place in the waiting-room of Madame Parvenu's Domestic Agency, South Kensington.

(The curtain rises to reveal Snout sitting in one of a dozen armchairs, examining his boot. To him, enter Antonio and Ignacia.)

ANTONIO   Buenos dias!
SNOUT   I come here by boot.
There is a long pause.
IGNACIA   Woddy say?
ANTONIO   E say e gum ere by boot.
IGNACIA   O! Wi gum ere by boot, also! Wi gum ere wid *S. S. Malateste* in 1972!
They perform handsprings. Snout feels inside his boot.
SNOUT   I picked up a stone in Osbaldeston Road. Probably at the junction with Pondicherry Crescent.

94

IGNACIA	I PICK UP A STONE IN IVER HEATH! I gum to bloody Stoppard ouse, I weigh one hundred pounds, pretty soon I fat like pig.
ANTONIO	She never see bourbon biscuits before. Is ole new world. Is one reason we get bullet. One day, she eat ten packs pinguins.
SNOUT	Or possibly at the point where Mafeking Villas runs parallel with the North Circular. You would not believe the amount of gravel they have put down there. Gravel and loose shale. Loose shale and chippings.
ANTONIO	One day, she eat ten pounds chippings.
SNOUT	Had I come by bus this situation would not have arisen. It would not have come about. Had I taken a Number Fourteen, I could have transferred to a Number Twenty-nine as far as Turnpike Lane. I could then have taken the underground. I could have gone down into the underground. I could have hopped aboard the underground, as it were. My boots would have been completely safe against shale on the underground. Manor House, Finsbury Park, Arsenal. I might have come up at any point.
ANTONIO	Mr Stoppard give us heave-ho.
IGNACIA	E say we no good. E say we bad.
ANTONIO	So I say to im: wod you min, good, wod you min, bad? You min good/bad in metaphysical sense, you blidding ponce? You min good/bad in empirical sense? You min good/bad in comparative descriptive sense?
IGNACIA	You tole im all right! You say: Wod about them situations where it is better to be bad than good? You say: Wod about definin your terms, you iggerant sod?
ANTONIO	E look at me a long time after that. Then e it me wid a double-boiler.
IGNACIA	Then we give notice.

They perform double back-somersaults, with half-gainers.

SNOUT	Alternatively, I could have called a cab. I could have hailed a cab. It might have set me down on

the wrong side of Pontings, of course, if it had come down Kensington Church Street, and I would have been compelled to have crossed the road by the Kentucky Pancake House, walked up as far as the Alpine Restaurant at the bottom of Campden Hill Road, and then taken a Number Nine to Hyde Park Corner. If he wasn't so mean. If Pinter wasn't so bleeding tight. If he wasn't so sodding stingy. (*He begins to rub his lapel, vigorously*) I had no severance pay. I was given no notice. I was offered no compensation in the way of, in lieu of, as an alternative to, I WAS NOT GIVEN TWO HALFPENNIES TO RUB TOGETHER, CONTRARY TO WHAT IS CLEARLY SPECIFIED BY THE LAWS OF THE LAND NOW OBTAINING!

Enter Sadie
SADIE   You bring up playwrights, what do you get? Heartaches you get. Ulcers you get. Possibly a malignant disease. You feed him, he shouldn't get God forbid a chill on the liver, all weathers he goes out in to meet his arty friends, I wouldn't give you a thank you for them, you lay out Sea Island cotton underwear for him. Comfort you already washed it in, it should be nice and soft, it shouldn't give him God forbid a rash on his little pippick. Also it should be nice and clean and a credit to his dear parents, may they rest in peace, they worked, they slaved, in case God forbid he should get knocked down and taken to hospital, you hang garlic flowers round his windows in case God forbid a vampire should get in one night he's not looking, he's lying there, he's drunk from his lousy friends, he's worn out from whatever it is he does all day, such as nothing, which is what he does all day, his poor father should only see him, years he stood in that shop, varicose veins, an enlarged prostate, when they took it out they needed three surgeons, three qualified men, just to carry it out of the operating theatre, but does *he* care? He used his flat like it was a hotel, you use this flat like it

96

was a hotel, I used to tell him, it's *my* flat, he used to say. You're answering back already? I used to enquire, you're already too big to take criticism, Mr Playwright, Mr Big Shot, you're too old to listen to people, Mr Show Business?

SNOUT   Or I could have crossed over when I got to the Alpine Restaurant and gone down the underground next to Derry and Toms.

ANTONIO   I miss Tom and Derry. I say to Mr Stoppard, why wi no got colour tee vee, you bum, as per Ome Office regulations? E reply television is a bastard word, it not exist, philologically spikkin, as it do not exist, wi do not ave it. I tell im, if it do not exist, wod is all that flickerin across the road?

IGNACIA   I say, ow you define exist, wod terms wi dealing wid ere? Then e it me wid a liquidiser.

ANTONIO   Then wi give notice again.

SADIE   Also, Mr Shakespeare, Mr Impresario, while we're on the subject, I said, when was the last time you had a play on in the West End, all of a sudden you're complaining about my work, I haven't got also the right to complain about the work of some people I could mention, they're not standing a million miles away from me, as it happens, God forbid I should mention any names, you think it's nice for *me*, I said, I'm standing in the butcher's you should have a nice piece calf's liver, a chop, a fresh portion sidebowler, and people say: Well, Sadie, did he write anything new yet, a classic, possibly, a musical, maybe, tunes you can whistle?

SNOUT   I am also prepared to blame *her*. I am also prepared to blame his leman. I am also prepared to lay certain charges at the foot of his paramour.

SADIE   So he sacked me.

SNOUT   Now he is living with me, she said, now he is living with me, she remarked, I should be grateful if you would take yourself in hand. I do not require a caretaker, she expatiated. I require a butler. (*He begins to pick furiously at a shredding buttonhole*) I WAS ENGAGED AS A CARETAKER, I told her, I WAS

ENGAGED TO BRING IN THE COKE, TO POLISH FRONT STEP TO REQUIRED STANDARD, TO ENSURE TRADESPEOPLE CAME ROUND TO SIDE DOOR! I AGREED UNDER THE TERMS OF SAID EMPLOYMENT TO WEAR A KHAKI WAREHOUSE COAT, BUT TO PROVIDE OWN STRING FOR KNEEPADS, I informed her, THERE WAS NEVER ANY QUESTION OF BUTTLING, THERE WAS NEVER ANY QUESTION OF THAT AT ALL!

Enter Fifi

FIFI Ooh la-la! Ma knickers ave disappear! Ah ad zem when ah lef zer ouse! Where can zey bi? Can eet bi e av stuff zem bah mistek in is brifcase for zer umpteence time? Sank God ah ave lef is employ at last! Ah do not ask for much in zis life, only an employer oo does not expeck mi to spen alf zer day in zer wardrobe. (*Faints. Bra falls off.*)

SNOUT I WAS NOT ENGAGED TO MINCE ABOUT WITH A SILVER BLEEDING TRAY, I explained to her. IT WAS NOT AN UNDERTAKING WHICH APPEARED ON MY CARDS!

Enter Hodge, backwards

HODGE Thank you very much, sir. Will there be anything else?

IGNACIA Woddy say?

HODGE I do beg your pardon, madame. I have grown somewhat used to backing into rooms. At Mr Ayckbourn's, do you see, all the rooms were always filled with people, invariably called Ron, Reg, Alf, Sid, Ned, Norman, or Don. There were usually two or three Maureens on the premises, and on one occasion, five Beryls. They were all related to one another, though not always in immediately apparent ways. They tended to drift from one part of the house to the other and carry on extraordinarily confusing conversations under the mistaken assumption that one knew what they were talking about. It was very convenient for Mr Ayckbourn, who used to walk about with two typewriters and a running tape-recorder, thus enabling himself to knock off several tetralogies a week by the simple expedient of overhearing, but it was most confusing for, ahem, a gentleman's gentleman. It has been said, though not, I hasten to add by me, that these people were not Mr Ayckbourn's acquaintances at all, but retained by his several agents on a salaried, if tiny, basis. In any event, I have left his service to seek employment elsewhere, despite the fact that I have no references: when I asked for them, my employer began to type on both machines simultaneously, and by lunchtime they had turned into an eighteen-part sit-com series for ATV.

SNOUT   BUTTLING, I riposted, *BUTTLING?* I should rather, I should prefer, I should be more willing to take my chances as a conductor on a 737 Greenline bus, commencing at Marble Arch, continuing down Edgware Road, along Maida Vale, up Kilburn High Road as far as the point where Cricklewood Lane crosses Cricklewood Broadway, bearing right past the point at which the old Handley Page aeroplane factory used to. . . .

The light begins to fade. Snout's monologue drones on, counterpointed, after an hour or so, by the sound, from the corridor, of Mrs Gland beating Spot Douglas-Home with a rhinestone-studded riding crop as
THE CURTAIN FALLS

THE EXPANDING OBSERVER

TRAIN ROBBERS' OWN STORY
This man now selling flowers outside Waterloo Station was one of the ring... carried out the... Their...

SUNDAY TIMES
weekly review
MAY 7 1978

KITCHENS
May Issue
Family Circle

The confessions of Bertie Smalls

● Over four years in the late Sixties and early Seventies a highly fluid group of armed robbers successfully seized over £1 million in raids on banks and security vehicles. But in August 1972, following a raid on Barclays bank in Wembley (left) in which £138,000 was sto... breakthrough came for the

THE SUNDAY TELEGRAPH   MAY 7, 1978

WATERGATE: Richard Nixon on the miscalculation and corruption that led to the cover-up

Where I went wrong

THE NIXON VERSION

Bloody Sunday

AT 11.04 precisely on the morning of Friday, May 12, a short, stocky man walked through the swing-doors into the reception area of *The Sunday Times* in London's famed Gray's Inn Road.

He was wearing a fifteen-denier Polly Peck stocking mask in Acapulco Peach, and carrying a sawn-off double-barrelled twelve-bore Jewell & Warriss shotgun. He paused to glance about him, and in that moment of hesitation a uniformed security guard sprang lithely towards him.

'Ronnie Smalls!' cried the guard, 'alias Piers Paul Weasel! I'd know that mask anywhere!'

Smalls took a step backwards. He cocked the gun. It was 11.05.

'Who's that?' he hissed.

'*Who's that?* It's me! Buster "Milhous" Perrott! We done the Wembley Tesco's together. I was the wheels, remember?'

'Stone me!' shouted Smalls. 'I know that voice! I can't see nothing through this bloody thing.'

'Don't tell *me*,' said the guard, 'I was there when you shot that pyramid of Kennomeat on account of it wouldn't lie down on the floor.'

100

He took the masked man by the right elbow and led him into a broom-cupboard beside the lifts. It was 11.07.

'So,' said Smalls to a mop, 'You're in security now, are you? Very nice. Got anything on?'

'I'm over here,' said the guard. 'Yes, I'm knocking off a four-part series for the Colour Magazine entitled HOW BENT ARE OUR PRIVATE ARMIES? There's five grand in it.'

'Very sweet.' Smalls sighed. 'I never got nothing out of that Wembley job, you know. It all went to that tall sod who hit the assistant manager with an axe.'

'I saw,' muttered the guard. 'First weekend after we went to ground I opened my *Sunday Express*, and there it was: I WAS THAT TALL SOD WHO HIT THE ASSISTANT MANAGER WITH AN AXE. First of a six-part series. As told to James Herriot. Artist's reconstruction of frozen veg counter by Francis Bacon.'

'Got to be worth ten grand,' murmured Smalls.

'Easy,' said the guard. 'Werl, you got to have the violence in, these days. Photo of ginger hairs taken from blade of Exhibit B, all that.'

And then he hit Smalls behind the left ear, very neatly, with a sockful of pesetas. A nice, bizarre touch, perfect for a cross-heading.

It was 11.09.

At 12.02 exactly, Ronnie Smalls crawled out of the lift at the fourth floor and staggered along the corridor until he reached the office of the Serious Crimes Editor. He pushed open the ribbed-glass door, and fell on the beige cord carpet.

The Serious Crimes Editor leapt from his chair.

'Watch it!' he cried. 'That is the Sunday Times Beige Cord Carpet Club Offer, only £2.95 a metre, and you're bleeding on it.'

'Yes,' said Smalls, faintly, 'I have just been mugged by Buster "Milhous" Perrott.'

'I know,' snapped the Serious Crimes Editor, 'he insisted on inserting a paragraph to that effect ten minutes ago. It hasn't half cocked up our layout, I don't mind telling you. We may very well have to drop the exclusive photo showing private security chiefs drinking gin from the waders belonging to

Buster's Mexican mistress at the Black Pussy Casino & Grill, Romford. What do *you* want?'

Smalls got uncertainly to his feet, and indicated the shotgun.

'I have just turned over the Clerkenwell Road branch of the Natwest,' he declared.

'Oh, really? Many dead?'

Smalls coughed, embarrassed.

'They got these plastic screens up,' he said. 'You'd need a bazooka.'

The Serious Crimes Editor stared at him.

'What was the take?'

'It happened a bit fast,' said Smalls.

'What was the take?'

Smalls felt in his windcheater pocket.

'I got a lot of these little booklets about deposit accounts,' he said.

The Serious Crimes Editor pressed his buzzer.

'Mr Deighton? I wonder, might I borrow the lads for a moment?'

Ten seconds later, the door opened. Two megamorphic things blotted out the light.

'We was just telling him about how we put that geezer's bonce in the duck-press,' complained the first Beverley Brother.

'We was in the middle of thinking,' said the second.

'Sorry, boys,' said the Serious Crimes Editor. 'I need someone thrown out.'

The great heads swivelled. With fearful smiles, they split.

'Hallo, Ronnie,' they said.

It was 12.16.

At 2.13 pm, an excited editorial team picked Ronnie Smalls up from the steps of *The Observer* in Queen Victoria Street, where he had been dumped, and carried him inside.

'He might have been held six weeks in sado-masochistic Egham love-nest by crazed nymphomaniac Wee Free bishop!' cried a Senior Circulation Executive.

'No, no!' shrieked the Trashy Docufiction Editor. 'That shotgun wrapped around his neck, those shreds of stocking-mask stuffed in his mouth – this man is clearly a villain himself!'

'We could be sitting on a gold-mine!' shouted a Downmarket Consultant. 'Is this the Wirral rapist from whom terrified streetwalkers flee in horror? Could it be the head of the Dorking wing of the Provisional Irgun Zwei Meinhoff Brigade? Or possibly The Man Interpol Has Dubbed The Scorpion Who Now Tells All To Desmond Morris See Page Nine Inside?'

Beside themselves with happy anticipation, they dragged their unconscious prize before the Really Senior Edior (who had been appointed only that week to make sure that the Senior Editor saw to it that the Editor realised that the Absolutely Senior Editor took two lumps in his morning tea), and propped him in a chair.

'Who has he eaten?' snapped the Really Senior Editor. He was a direct man, and this was always his first question.

'We haven't spoken to him yet,' replied the Downmarket Consultant.

'Look in his pockets,' snapped the RSE, 'you might find a foot, or something. We could rush it up to Forensic.'

As the staff duly pulled Ronnie Smalls this way and that, he woke.

'I am prepared to blow the whistle on all of them,' he croaked. 'It will be the greatest grass in the history of smart journalism. Bring me Graham Greene. I have been done over by the Beverley Brothers.'

'What?' yelled the Trashy Docufiction Editor. '*The* Beverley Brothers, alias the Andrews Brothers, formerly known as the Dolly Brothers? We have been trying to get our hands on them for years! We have had men scouring Patagonia, we have dropped three counterfeit lamas into Sing Sing, we have left no stone un—where are they?'

'They're both over at *The Sunday Times*,' gasped the battered Smalls.

They dropped him back in his chair.

'*What?*'

The Really Senior Editor began clearing his desk.

'This is the end of sophisticated Sunday journalism as we know it,' he muttered. 'Or as I know it, anyway. *The Observer* is done for, lads! I shall be at The Seaview Elite Boarding House, Grand Cayman, if anyone wants me.'

Smalls sat up, recovering.

'Yes, I could prob'ly let you have the whole story for—what?—fifteen thousand. 'Course, I'd expect to reserve film rights, then there's translations on top, plus an agreed percentage of—'

The Really Senior Editor glared down at him malevolently.

'Call the police!' he barked.

At 2.44 pm, two detective constables from East End Central burst through the editorial doors.

'Bang to rights, Ronnie!' shouted the first, gathering the little crook's collar.

'Hang about,' said Smalls quickly, 'there's a pony in this for you.'

The first constable paused.

'Is that each?' he enquired.

The second constable drew his truncheon and laid it across his colleague's skull. The first constable sank to the floor in a loose serge pile.

'I was wondering,' said the second constable to a corner of the ceiling, 'whether there might not be a market for an eight-part series on corruption in the Met. In the cause of common decency, I name the guilty men. I do not shirk from penetrating the upper things, echelons. I lay bare countless secrets that have been kept from the British public for far too long. I have a numbered account at the Kreditanstalt, Zurich.'

The editorial staff cheered!

'This is not the end!' cried the Really Senior Editor, emptying his briefcase back onto the desk and plucking a contract therefrom. 'It is not even the beginning of the end! But it is, perhaps, the—'

From beneath the fallen constable, Ronnie Smalls painfully extracted his stricken body and crept, unnoticed, away.

It was 2.49 pm.

At 4.58, my office door opened and Ronnie Smalls hobbled in. Around his neck hung a heavy gilt frame. From it, he pulled a sliver of flaking canvas.

'It was the founder of *The Sunday Telegraph*,' he said. 'I just been up there.' He touched a filthy rag to his bloodstained nose.

'They expressed no interest in a follow-up to Nixon's Watergate confessions. I offered 'em all this stuff about the night I burgled 14a, Khartoum Villas and nearly got the radiogram out, only I stepped on the cat.'

'How much were you asking?' I enquired.

He sighed. It had clearly been a long day.

'To you,' he said, 'thirty bob.'

'I'll get my typewriter,' I said.

'You're a gent,' said Ronnie Smalls.

'I'm a journalist,' I replied.

After Strange Gods

'I was a good Mormon. I don't think people have any idea of what being a good Mormon means.'—Miss Joyce McKinney

IN THE EARLY post-revolutionary years of the United States, that is to say during the first two or three decades of the nineteenth century, the frontier traditions of individualism, dissent and evangelism combined and found expression in the formation of numerous religious and quasi-religious sects. The intellectually and morally restrictive liabilities of the myriad European traditions having been struck off, the New Americans, exulting in the seeming illimitability of their fresh freedoms, sought many new gods in which to vest the fundamentalist theological passions of the frontier.

The most striking and important of these faiths was Mormonism.

One spring day in 1829, near what is now Ithaca in upper New York State, a young man called Joseph McKinney walked into the woods, alone. It was there, by his own account, that two glorious personages appeared to him, apparelled, as he put it so memorably, in shimmering raiment. One of them was Big Sadie Wasserman, who scraped a living by posing for Sioux war parties dressed only in galoshes and epaulettes; the other was Dolores del Mooney, who ran The Raft Of A Thousand Delights on the Acopontohac River and was said to be able to smoke three cheroots at once without anyone noticing. Upon the young and impressionable Joseph, these two ladies left their ineradicable marks, at less than thirty cents a time. Joseph wrote everything down, and when, at the end of that extraordinary week, he re-emerged from the forest, his eyes ablaze with new fire, he held the entire text of that amazing work, *The Book of Mormon*.

At first, very few people back at the settlement could understand the arcane concepts and weird unfamiliar language, but they tore the pictures out and ran off with them. Over the ensuing days, they returned to the settlement in ones and twos, and occasionally threes, and begged Joseph to tell them more. Gripped now with missionary fervour and realising the magnitude of what he had discovered, the young McKinney contacted the angel Moroni who agreed to put up fifty per cent; together, they made *The Book* available to genuine collectors only and beat up anybody who tried to browse without buying. Within three weeks, *The Book* had toppled Puritan Crochet from its place at the top of the charts, and was well on the way to selling its first million. This, to get its amazing success into proper perspective, was well before Sir Rowland Hill had introduced the mail-order principle to the world: to get their copies of *The Book*, believers had to come round to the back of Joseph McKinney's first temple. He also sold stationery and pot plants, but *The Book* was where the money was.

There were girls upstairs, too, who helped with reading the difficult passages; but as the result of this, the temple was attacked by a Mafia raiding party from The Raft Of A Thousand Delights, and Joseph McKinney and his followers were driven out of New York and forced to flee westwards.

The First Great Trek was fraught with vicissitude. Day after day, the pitiful wagon train was fallen upon by Indians, who reckoned that forking out two whole bags of wampum entitled them to more than ten minutes. Their dissatisfaction with the service most usually expressed itself in summary scalping; by the fall of 1821, eighty per cent of Joseph McKinney's female flock were bald. The enraged disappointment this occasioned in the white settlements through which they passed, all of whom had bought copies of *The Book* and thus been led to expect a better quality Mormon product when they turned up at the wagons, almost put paid to Joseph's mission, especially as a rival faith, Gay Witnesses, was beginning to gain considerable ground in the logging camps of Illinois.

Joseph realised that his only course was to replenish his

depleted stocks of believers. Accordingly, he went once more into the lonely woods and prayed for a sign; when he came out again, it was to announce the principle of polygamy.

By this radical and visionary means, the mission's ranks were rapidly swollen with hundreds of young women, most of them refugees from the Irish Husband Famine. They were simple girls, and never cottoned on to the implications of the fact that they were all called Mrs McKinney. They all had, after all, a nice tin wedding ring, and were allowed to keep five per cent of their earnings as a dress allowance. Having been kept, back home, in total ignorance of married life, they found nothing odd about what was expected of them during the small hours, and generally thought it nice to meet so many new people all the time.

America was fulfilling, it seemed, its promises of golden opportunity.

By 1832, Joseph had made enough money to settle permanently in Illinois, at Nauvoo on the banks of the Mississippi, where he founded a university and commenced erecting a great temple.

It was a pretty good university. You couldn't learn much, but what you could learn it was pretty hard to get a degree for anywhere else. There were two years of theory, after which graduates were awarded the coveted Blue Flannel Suit. They then went out into the field for one year of practical work, which involved going from door to door throughout the United States distributing copies of *The Book* and trying to get chained to beds for folding money. Many housewives were converted this way, and subsequently paid a tithe of their income to Joseph. Once a year, on Graduation Day, a great convention was held at the Nauvoo temple. It went on for a week, and became famous throughout North America as the only annual convention to which you didn't have to bring secretaries.

But tragedy was soon to strike. Factioneering and apostasy were afflicting the community (some Elders wished to diversify into the blue lantern slide business, others felt that the future lay in escort agencies, still more felt passionately that they ought to be putting underwear out under their own label), and on the afternoon of June 27, 1844, Joseph McKinney was hanged by an irate mob of shareholders.

The problem of the succession to this great autocratic visionary was paramount.

But the times brought forth the man.

Brigham McKinney was Joseph's 733rd son. He bore a striking resemblance to his father (as, indeed, did everyone else), but he was unique in that he possessed an even stronger proselytising passion. Where Joseph was happy to control only a town, Brigham had his heart set upon running an entire state. That way you got to send Congressmen to Washington, thereby expanding your marketing area illimitably.

And the beauty of this was that, in the very year of his accession to the leadership, over in Paris Louis Daguerre had discovered that by fuming an exposed iodised silver plate with mercury vapour, you could produce a dirty postcard.

Brigham, with the acuity and wisdom that characterised and characterises all McKinneys, immediately saw the evangelical potential of photography. And it was this which led him, unerringly, to fix on Utah as his goal: 'This must be the place!' as he so famously cried. The point being that the quality of the light in Utah was unique (as John Ford subsequently realised) and very strong, so that shorter exposures, in those early days, were possible; always an aspect to be considered when you have a montage of eight young women, three old men, a dromedary, four pelicans and an anaconda to get down erotically on your plate before anyone moves.

And so it was that Brigham McKinney came to the Great Salt Lake, which gave back so much reflected light that it was possible to do in 1/25 of a second what no Frenchman had previously attempted to try in less than two minutes.

There was also a lot of cactus around for connoisseurs of the genre.

By 1850, the Mormon Trail extended along the banks of the Platte River as far as Fort Laramie, and every five miles there was a Pony Express station that sold calendars, inflatable latex pioneers, Mormon Fly, and peep-hole liberty bodices. And at the intersection with the Oregon Trail, Brigham McKinney set up a supermarket shopping precinct where it was possible to break anything up to seven commandments just by looking in the window.

Furthermore, when the railroad came, in 1869, Brigham was more than ready for it. Through a special deal with the Atcheson, Topeka, Wabash & Rock Island Company, he got the wagons-lits concession throughout the northern states; his were the only mixed sleeping-cars where the passengers travelled upright.

The rest is history. In the ensuing century, McKinney's movement went from strength to strength until, today, it boasts more than two million adherents world-wide, including eight hundred thousand singing families, who alone contain upwards of thirty million teeth. With the advent of tabloid journalism, their power and influence has extended beyond the most ambitious dreams of young Joseph McKinney, framed all those years ago amid the Ithacan ferns.

Of course, it is sometimes pointed out by the more cautious historians that there might be more to Mormonism than the image of overweight ex-beauty queens rolling around in the cheaper motel room while their agents dial the tawdrier editors of the civilized world, but it's a difficult argument to make stick any more.

The King and We

CONTRACTS & TENDERS

KINGDOM OF THAILAND
NOTICE TO
CIVIL ENGINEERING CONTRACTORS

The Government of the Kingdom of Thailand has received a loan from the World Bank to help finance construction of three roads totalling about 140km and expected to cost over U.S. $50 million equivalent. The construction will be divided into three contracts to be awarded in 1978 and 1979 and will include about six million cubic metres of earthworks, one million square metres of asphalt paving and six thousand lineal metres of bridges.

Construction firms from member countries of the World Bank and Switzerland are invited to indicate their interest in prequalifying for bidding on the above works. Replies, by letter or cable, should be addressed to:

DIRECTOR GENERAL,
DEPARTMENT OF HIGHWAYS,
SRI AYUTHAYA ROAD,
BANGKOK, THAILAND.

Replies should be received by 15th May, 1978, and questionaires will then be sent for preparation of prequalification applications.

The throne-room, Bangkok. The King of Siam sits, lopsidedly, on his formerly magnificent jewelled throne; the eyes are missing from the dragon-head arms, and one leg is propped up on a brick. The King is staring bleakly at what was once the finest tessellated floor in all Asia: it now has a huge zigzagged crack across its entire width, from which rats pop with unsettling nonchalance. The ninth-century stained glass windows have all fallen out, and been replaced with old plywood doors, a number of which have KILL THE PRODS! and STUF THE POPE! aerosoled across them. Somewhere close by, a compressor starts up and the last remaining chandelier falls to the floor in a crystal explosion. The King leaps up, and bangs his head on the crumbling wall.

KING   BRING ME MISTER ANNER!

A courtier, white with plaster-dust, shuffles out. After two or three minutes, thunderous concussions shake the throne-room until a large hole appears in the wall facing the King. Through this, sledgehammer in hand, steps Norman Anner, construction supervisor of the British company which has successfully tendered for the Bangkok Ring Road contract. As he moves away from the new hole, a vista is presented of the former park beyond. A bulldozer race seems to be in progress; trees fall, navvies cheer, the Ladbroke stand is doing a roaring trade.

KING   WHAT IS GOING ON?

ANNER   Ah. *(Sings, as navvies down tools, file through hole, and set up fifty-piece Irish Show Band)*:

111

Getting the ground dug,
Getting the holes nice and wossname!
Getting the turf up,
Getting to knock down each tree!
Smashing the statues
Seems to be going nicely—
Werl, that's precisely
Our cup of tea!

At these last words, the band immediately knocks off, brews up, unwraps bread pudding, deals cards, etc. The court waits. After half an hour, the band and the singer resume:

Getting the piers, soon,
Getting 'em all sent from Tilbury!
Be here by Christmas,
Or possibly by Easter Day.
Depends on the . . .

The King leaps up again, trembling.

KING   But this was supposed to be a ring road, I expressly asked for a Bangkok by-pass, the whole point was to save my beautiful capital from ruin, from despoliation, from . . .

ANNER   Sorry, squire, I am just carrying out wossnames, I am not responsible for the architect, I only follow the plans, don't I? Werl, that's to say, where possible, know what I mean? Want my opinion, your best course is to have a word with our friend Mister . . .

The King snaps his fingers, the courtier hobbles out again, returning after some delay with a plump Englishman, a napkin at his neck, half a lobster in his hand. He is whistling.

KING   (*screams*) YOU ARE RESPONSIBLE FOR DRIVING A SIX-LANE MOTORWAY THROUGH THE MOST BEAUTIFUL CITY IN THE WORLD! WHAT GIVES YOU THE RIGHT TO WHISTLE?

ARCHITECT   (*removes sliver of seafood from bicuspid with gold tooth-pick, and sings*)
Whenever I cock things up,
They're generally cocked up big,

So I whistle a happy tune,
So's nobody will twig
What's gone wrong!

While wondering why new flats
Have fallen to the ground,
I whistle a happy tune
And buy another round.
Cheers! So long!

(*Tosses empty lobster aside, pirouettes gaily*)

The result of these deceptions,
Is: *nobody suspects!*
And mayors throw big receptions
To thank the architects!

Remember my M14?
It ended up a wall,
And everybody thought . . .

The architect is informed that his soufflé à la manière de la Vicomtesse de Bragalonne is ready, and exits, dancing, left, to make way for The March of the Irish Navvies. These endearing little folk, resplendent in traditional donkey jackets are desperate to win the affection of the King their master by showing him what they have learned during their long training. The routine is a show-stopper: at one time, thirty-six of them are leaning on a single shovel (is it hypnosis? auto-suggestion? fakirism? sheer magic?) while twenty-four more stand on their heads in a firkin of Guinness. The King, however, is a stern father to his people, and chooses not to show how charmed he is, preferring instead to fall down and foam at the mouth.

As he does so, the right hand wall of his palace disappears. When the priceless mediaeval dust clears, a sixty-ton mechanical excavator is revealed. The driver dismounts.

DRIVER   Is this where the underpass is going?

The King swoons, is revived, and calls feebly for his Borough Surveyor. Construction boss Norman Anner is taken aback, but recovers upon recognising the Borough Surveyor, who turns out to be not a Thai but an Englishman imported by the misguided King from Camden Council. The Borough Surveyor bows before the monarch.

SURVEYOR	Can I be of assistance, your majesty?
KING	Stop them, Wisbeech! Ply them with injunctions, smite them with local authority codicils, stay them with . . . (*faints again*)
SURVEYOR	Ah. (*Sings*): Hello, young navvies! You can't move that drain, Without Form 49b. Besides, all the bye-laws specifically state You may not demolish a tree. Hello! Gorblimey! You're joking, of course? That gully was not on the plans! And as for them bleeding great overhead pipes, The matter is out of my hands. Do you know what it takes To drain thirty-one lakes, As requested in yours of the 1st? Have you any idea? We got work up to here— Not to mention, er, terrible thirst!

(*He stares hard at Norman Anner, for some seconds. Anner reaches into his breast-pocket, at last.*)

> A drink? 'Ow civil!
> Well, I won't say no;
> I am dealing, I see here, with gents!
> I imagine five hundred would—nudge, nudge, wink, wink!—
> Help to cover our extra expense!

Borough Surveyor pockets plain brown envelope, and exits left. The sixty-ton mechanical excavator begins to eat the roof. The King wrings his hands, courtiers roll around moaning, concubines pelt the intruders with Carmen rollers, all to no avail. Finally, as a dynamiting error brings a sacred belfry cascading into the throne-room, the King struggles to his feet and shrieks:

114

KING   CAN NOBODY SAVE MY POOR KINGDOM?

There is an embarrassing silence, punctuated only by some uneasy hemming and hawing, until the Irish navvies, ever sensitive to the King's mercurial moods, begin to glance speculatively at one another across the pitiful debris. At last, they form themselves into a loose beery phalanx, and sing:

CHORUS   Shall we strike?
                     POM! POM! POM!
                     Shall we put down our shovels and walk out?
                     POM! POM! POM!
                     Shall we strike?
                     POM! POM! POM!
                     Shall we knock off and open up the stout?
                     POM! POM! POM!
                     Well, begob!
                     We have been here since Thursday, after all!
                     POM! POM! POM!
                     And the plain simple fact is
                     It is now accepted practice
                     That we do what we bleeding like—
                     On the clear understanding
                     That this kind of thing can happen,
                     Shall we strike? Shall we strike? Shall we strike?

They strike. The navvies troop out, the excavator backs away, Norman Anner rolls up his plans, the architect falls asleep in his mousse, and a great soft silence descends on Bangkok.

When, a day or so later, the Khmer Rouge forces pour over the Cambodian border, they are, to their considerable surprise, welcomed by the King with what, to the casual eye, looks remarkably like gratitude.

The Way to the Stars

The White Paper recommends that Biggin Hill should be taken over by the British Airports Authority and developed for businessmen's executive planes.—Daily Mail

OUTSIDE THE OLD green Nissen hut, the businessmen dozed in the sun. Black labradors dozed at their feet. True, here and there the drone of bees was punctuated by the click of backgammon counters, but such activity was the exception. Dozing was the rule.

They lay sprawled in their canvas chairs beneath the blue Kent sky, their rippling blond toupees ruffled by the summer breeze, their suede flying-waistcoats unbuttoned, their heavy cufflinks bulled to Brasso glitter, their smooth pink faces slack with sleep. The fatigue was palpable: the Glenlivet, the profiteroles, the plump grouse and the plumper secretaries had all taken their inevitable toll.

So much was asked of them, this pitiful handful of Englishmen and their old-fashioned string-and-paper enterprises, nothing between them and the might of Germany and Japan but obsolete techniques and half-trained crews, flying gamely (but blind) into enemy territory with only last year's address books as their guide, against appalling odds. Mere boys, many of them no more than forty-five, they had been plucked from their playing-fields and hurled into family businesses with no formal training whatever, left to muddle along on such skills as they had managed to pick up at Tramp and Annabel's.

Yet, as the storm clouds gathered, darkling, over England, they had not been found wanting: they had rallied to the call, they had flocked out to Biggin and Tangmere in their company

116

Mercs and Alfas, and, unshaken by the fearful threat poised across the narrow Channel, dozed off.

In the makeshift Ops Room, while yawning escort agency girls with weary eyes pushed their wooden rakes across the European map like the croupiers as which they nightly doubled, dragging the ominous massed blobs of Yamaha and Braun and Fiat ever deeper into British territory, the Group Sales Manager of Polygunk Industries placed a small cardboard box in front of his aide.

'The boffins have come up with this,' he said quietly.

The aide opened the box.

'What is it, sir?' he said.

The GSM smiled.

'It baffled me, too, at first, old chap,' he said. 'Amazing technical breakthrough, actually. It's a post-Jubilee chiming beefeater that holds anything up to five cigarettes. Every hour on the hour it plays *Puppet On A String*, our great Eurovision triumph, and walks up and down for a bit.'

'Good Lord!' cried the aide. 'Is there no end to Barnes Wallis's genius?'

'Our plan,' said the GSM, 'is to hit them hard in three different places, Hanover, Wuppertal, Dortmund, all in a single sortie! What do you think of *that*, Frobisher?'

The aide narrowed his steel-blue eyes.

'It might just work,' he said.

He wound up the beefeater.

Its head fell off.

The Senior Export Flight Controller limped into the Briefing Hall. So did his dog. They both had tin legs. Neither leg, unfortunately, hinged at the knee; new bolts had been on order for eighteen months. Even more unfortunately, the dog's ended in a man's tin foot, all tin paws having been recalled the year before by the manufacturers because of a design fault.

The air in the hall was thick with Hai Karate and the sound of snoring, but the assembled businessmen were suddenly snapped awake by the dog, which, attempting to scratch itself with its giant iron hind-limb, fell over with a clang.

'Chaps!' barked the SEFC. 'I'd like you to look at this!'

He whipped back the green baize cover from the blackboard beside him. The men gasped!

'Yes,' said the Controller, 'the writing's fallen off it. Is the Chairman of Belwether British Chalks here, by any chance?'

A large flier in a pin-striped charcoal-grey Mae West stood up.

'Sorry about that,' he said, 'we seem to have supplied an export-only batch in error. You should've got our Premier Non-Squeak Number 4.'

'Are you telling me,' snapped the Controller, 'that my plucky, hard-pressed golden lads are risking their lives flying worthless chalk into the enemy heartland?'

'It's only going to bloody Chad,' protested Belwether. 'They don't know how to write there, anyhow. When the chalk don't mark, they'll think it's them. By the time they learn different, we were planning to get taken over by Reeves or somebody. No harm done.'

'No harm done?' cried the SEFC. 'I was up all night putting our flight plan on that! In two hours, you will be hitting the Ruhr with eight million giant rubber spiders! They're loading the suitcases and folding tables *now*!'

Among those businessmen who had not yet dozed off again, there was uproar.

'Novelty goods?' shrieked a thin salesman in the front row. 'Have you any idea what chance we stand against Jerry with those, sir?'

'He's right, sir,' called another. 'On our last run to Düsseldorf, we were cut to pieces! Schlimmhalters of Essen are capable of putting out ersatz Gonks at three quid a gross! The Essen Rubbischverein alone has a weekly output of five hundred metric tonnes of plastic dogs' doings, and the Wiesengross whoopee cushion is light years ahead of anything we can do. Give us something we can get our teeth into, sir, give us something big to throw at them!'

'Give us a car!' piped a voice.

'Who's that?' barked the Controller.

'Phillimore, sir.'

'You're just up from base, aren't you, Phillimore?' said the

Controller, not unkindly.

'Yes, sir.'

'I thought so. Only a sprog would bring up cars. These are dark days for the economy, Phillimore. I'm told we shall be getting a new British Leyland Medium Mini Maxi Sports Caravanette Hatchback by 1993, but until then, Phillimore, we shall just have to stiffen the old lip, shan't we, bite on the thingy, make do and mend, eh?'

'Yes, sir. Sorry, sir.'

'Splendid!' said the Controller. 'Now chaps, let's get into the old crates and show Jerry what we're made of! And remember, if you meet any foreigners, try not to give the game away by talking. They speak a different language, most of 'em, and if they suspect you're British you won't stand a bloody chance! Try to make contact with our agents on the ground, they sometimes know a shop or two which might take a dozen. Good hunting! By God, I wish I was going with you!'

And here he thwacked his tin leg with his stout malacca cane. A nut dropped out, and rolled under the table.

'Wake up, Frobisher!' cried the Group Sales Manager. 'They're coming back!'

The two men shielded their eyes against the rising sun.

They craned.

They peered.

'My God,' muttered Frobisher, 'he's on his own!'

The GSM steadied himself against the parapet of the control tower.

'Five gone, old lad,' he whispered. 'Five failed to return!'

They walked slowly to the De-Briefing Room to meet the sole survivor.

'We lost Harrison on the way over,' he said. His eyes were glazed, his voice cracked. 'He has decided to take up residence in Guernsey. Webster managed the trip all right, put down in Bruges to ask the way, and had his bloody plane impounded against the non-fulfilment of an order for Chelsea boots going back to 1969. They got Morris before he was even off the Dortmund tarmac. They'd remembered him from when he was Morris's Corned Beef. They lost ninety people in that typhoid epidemic, you know, plus three decapitated by exploding tins. As for Jackson, I'm afraid the Reeperbahn got him on his first morning.'

He poured himself a large Hine, tremblingly.

'And Cox?' muttered the Controller. 'What about Cox?'

'Cox?' cried the survivor. He laughed a short bitter laugh. 'Don't talk to me of that treacherous swine, sir! Cox is staying there, sir, and good riddance, say I! Wuppertal Museum offered him fifty quid for his Trident, and he took it.'

Outside the old green Nissen hut, the businessmen dozed in the sun. Black labradors dozed at their feet. They did not wake even when, at precisely 14.00 hours, in impeccable formation and with a cataclysmic roar, three thousand Japanese executive Zeros dived without warning out of the dazzling sun.

When they did wake, however, everyone immediately agreed that it was an absolutely infamous way to do business.

Flying Dutchman

or

A TRAVEL firm yesterday offered air trips to America for 25p.

The sensational give-away stunned rival operators.

The scheme was launched in Amsterdam by the Dutch charter firm Gefau.

CALL ME PASSEPARTOUT.

Should you ask why, I should have to reply, in my mortification, that it is because my shoes are bound together with adhesive tape. In the old days, you could have called me Ishmael. That, of course, was before Ishmael Properties went down the tubes to the tune of £104,000,000 with so little warning that the only thing I managed to put in my wife's name were my brown brogues.

Which goes some way towards explaining why, upon that misty evening, I was standing at the Formica counter of the Reform Tea Bar on the Thames Embankment, munching a remaindered cream cracker and pondering how Formica had managed to make a go of it. Indeed, such was the depth of my despair, I was on the point of wondering whether I should not be well advised to cross the road and end it all in the ebon swirl below, when, as destiny would have it, another gentleman of the road hove to alongside, ordered a cheese roll, put down a crumpled pound note, and looked at his change.

'Bleeding stroll on!' he exclaimed. 'Twenty pee for an old

121

tennis ball with a slice of bloody Sunlight in it! Where will it all end?'

A rhetorical cry, that needed no answer; yet, at that moment, a member whom I had adjudged to be sleeping against the Reform's front wheel, suddenly opened his yellow eyes.

'If *I* had eighty pee,' he murmured, 'I'd emigrate.'

We looked at him.

'You would not,' said the newcomer, spreading his eight florins on the bar, 'get bleeding far on this. Personally, I doubt whether the cost of living is much lower in Fulham. You could not wake to a better life in Turnpike Lane. The fleshpots of Lewisham have not been widely advertised.'

At this, the other man stood up, and opened his threadbare greatcoat. Beneath, he wore a *Daily Mirror*; and from his left breast there shrieked the legend *NEW YORK FOR 25p!*

The man behind the counter whistled softly.

'I wouldn't mind betting,' he said, 'you could go around the world on eighty pee.'

There was a strange silence. A gull mewed. A foghorn moaned.

'Wouldn't mind betting what?' said the man with the cheese roll.

The bartender reflected; shrugged.

'Tell you what,' he said. 'You go round the world on that, come back here to the Reform with evidence, and I will personally stand you to a double egg, chips, beans, and two slices.'

'Done!' cried the man with the cheese roll.

They shook hands.

'I shall require you to take an observer,' said the bartender, 'whom I shall personally stand his own eighty pee to ensure the rules are respected.'

I stepped forward.

'Passepartout,' I said.

'Fogg,' said the man with the cheese roll.

I pocketed the Reform coins, and, turning our faces west, we set off.

The walk to Gatwick took ten hours by the drizzled moon, but at least the time gave me the opportunity to learn something of my companion. Fogg, it transpired, was a former Crown Commissioner who had drawn the short straw in his departmental lottery and thus been required to take responsibility for eight hundred million pounds. He had, of course, shouldered it without a murmur. The whole operation had been very British.

At Gatwick, our first task was to find an economical route to Schiphol Airport, since it was from Amsterdam that the 25p transatlantic flights embarked. Fogg was in favour of a Laker 3p Tuesday Dawn Return to Knokke, which bypassed IATA regulations by offering in-flight Communion to enable the aircraft to be re-classified as a cathedral, but I finally persuaded him to shell out the extra money and fly direct to Amsterdam on an Air Angola 5p Weekday Golden Special, a fare made possible by the fact that Angola had formally declared war on the Netherlands and persuaded IATA that reconnaissance missions stood outside their jurisdiction. It meant that Fogg and I had to parachute into Schiphol, but the time saved was invaluable.

Our companions aboard the subsequent Atlantic flight were a motley, though fascinating, company. I sat beside a somewhat lugubrious Dutch businessman called Hertz van Rental whose company had given him a first-class to Delhi where he was expected to initiate a flourishing Gouda import business by persuading the Indians that the cheese had been made from unconsecrated cows and was therefore permissible. The little hopes he had entertained for his success dwindled to nothing when he realised he could chop in his ticket for a 25p single to New York and receive an untaxed eight hundred pounds in return. He told me that he hoped to persuade his employers that, as a good Dutchman, he had always thought of New York as Nieuw Amsterdam, which was how the confusion over his destination had arisen in his mind; he would then return from New York, having spent the eight hundred pounds on, he hoped, Doris Day (his only passion), and explain its disappearance as cab-fares.

I told him that I thought his chances of successful deception slim, but he pointed out that a company which believed you could sell Gouda to Hindus might well believe anything.

123

I saw little of Fogg during the flight, since he had opted for the 14p economy class, and was travelling on the rudder.

Upon arrival at Kennedy, we found our choices myriad. We shopped around (though not without difficulty, Fogg by this time being stone-deaf and suffering from frostbite in both hands) and decided that the best deal was being offered by Gonniff Airlines, which was operating trans-continental flights into Los Angeles as a tax-loss. When the Federal Aviation Authority had raised understandable objections to the ten-cent fare, Gonniff had revealed that they were now operating as a charity designed to carry the blind to the western seaboard so that they could sniff the Pacific. In consequence, passengers at the Gonniff terminal were handed dark glasses and white sticks, a handicap unfortunately compounded in Fogg's case by his deafness and his frostbite, so that, unable to hear, see, or feel his way with his cane, he had to be winched aboard the 747 and carried, such were the strictures placed upon the handling crew by their union, as freight.

It was only when he was re-delivered into my hands at Los Angeles smelling strongly of ageing cheese that I realised that the owner of the samples must have been somewhere aboard. I consequently looked for him on the bus taking us to smell the ocean (Gonniff were fearful of FAA spies), and found him up front enquiring of the driver whether he would accept fifty dollars to drop him in Beverly Hills, preferably within walking distance of the Day residence.

The driver, however, declined, and returned us to Los Angeles airport, where Fogg and I soon thereafter took off for Tokyo.

As we were now down to less than a pound between us, Fogg and I decided to take advantage of an extraordinarily inviting Nippair offer to fly us to Japan for a mere five cents apiece. Upon enquiry, we were told that IATA had authorised the fare-breach on the grounds that the flight was for the exclusive use of Japanese war-veterans, a category that might have proved beyond our qualification had Fogg not managed to persuade

124

Nippair that during World War Two, we had both been traitors.

As a result, we found ourselves winging eastwards across the Pacific, tucking into our fourteenth free meal of the trip (and, incidentally, our fourteenth slice of ham with a pineapple ring on top), while our fellow passengers gathered around to watch with keen interest as Fogg struggled with his frost-charred fingers to chopstick the cherry garnish to his ravenous lip. They were a curiously sombre company, and it was not until we started our astonishingly sharp descent into Tokyo that we suddenly comprehended why. The captain's excited voice came over the intercom, first in Japanese, then, for our benefit, in English: 'This is your captain speaking. In two minutes we expect to dive onto the General Motors offices in Tokyo! Please unfasten your seatbelts and ignore the No Smoking signs!'

To impassioned shrieks of 'BANZAI!' our fellow passengers began tying flags to their foreheads, as Fogg and I stared in horror! Would it all end thus, with almost ninety pee still unspent?

Well might it have indeed, had not, at that very instant, a half-familiar figure risen to his feet, across the aisle, quickly becoming a fully familiar figure as he snatched out his orange-peel teeth and wiped the saffron staining from his cheeks. And suddenly, through the dense reek of joss, my nostrils perceived an old, and curiously welcome stench!

'Stop!' cried Hertz van Rental. 'Do you know who is currently playing in cabaret, for one week only, at the Tokyo Hilton?'

For a brief second, the fanatics paused, but it was time enough for the trusty Hollander to inform them that Doris Day would be singing such old favourites as *The Black Hills of Dakota*, *Moonlight Bay*, *It's Magic*, and many, many more. The Americano-Japs paused uncertainly, caught confused between two cultural magnets; and in that pause, atavism foundered. One or two began singing snatches of *Secret Love*, despite serious palatal difficulty, and in seconds it was all over.

The captain was informed of the change of plan, and five minutes later we were making a perfect three-point landing in Tokyo.

There is little more to tell. The second hemisphere of our historic journey was simplicity itself, for, upon arrival in Japan, we discovered that airline undercutting had, in our brief airborne absence, reached so hysterical a pitch that the companies were now vying with one another to pay passengers to fly with them! We compared offers, and found that El Al would not only pay us five hundred pounds apiece to fly first-class with them to Heathrow, they would also throw in a bespoke lounge suit with two pairs of pants, and pick up the cab-fare from Heathrow to the Reform! We were so taken aback, we even took the risk of asking the El Al agent in Tokyo how long they could continue running at a loss, and he agreed with us that it was crazy, but that they were temperamentally incapable of not wiping the floor with their competitors.

And so it was that, within hours, we were back at the Reform with £1,000.87 in our new mohair pockets, tucking into double egg, chips, beans, and two slices, while our fellow-members gazed on in rapt astonishment!

And while, too, far above us in the chill empyrean, out of reasonable excuses now and doomed forever thus to wander, growing richer yet more unsavoury by the minute, the hapless Hertz van Rental flew invisibly on.

Because It's There, Partly

'Eight middle-aged British businessmen plan to conquer a 20,000 ft unclimbed Himalayan peak, the Sattu.'—Daily Telegraph

BASE CAMP ONE: DAY ONE

I fear we have lost Ackroyd. Little short of a tragedy, so early in our quest. His personal assistant had a bust you could stand an ashtray on. I had great hopes of her for the final assault on the south col. There is, I have been given to understand, a small crevice just below the overhang large enough for only two people and a jeroboam.

There we are, though. I suppose I shall have to fall back on Miss Belwether again.

As it were.

Not that there was much likelihood of Ackroyd's seeing the thing through. He has always struck me as a cowardly little squirt, doubtless the result of having a mere 25% of the equity in Ackroyd Kwiklean Laundries. That he should have dropped out while we were still in Khatmandu was, however, a considerable shock: that a man is prepared to forego the great challenge that lies before us simply because there is a site for sale next to the Khatmandu Gaumont which, in Ackroyd's wretched words, cries out for a self-service dry-cleaning establishment with four desirable flats over plus adequate parking, seems to me to smack of the paltriness which has done so much to lay our great country low.

Should I perish on the peak, and should some public-spirited soul come upon this log beside my frozen corpse, I should rest in greater peace knowing that information had been passed to Mrs G. Ackroyd to the effect that her husband's personal assistant on this mission is not Mr Arthur Smales of accounts.

127

BASE CAMP ONE: DAY FOUR

The delay in starting is telling on us all. For four days now, our party has been waiting for Simpson to get his cigar lit. We have told him that the shortage of oxygen at 15,000 feet lies at the root of his problem, but he is a stubborn swine, as witness his refusal to diversify into extruded plastics. Every morning he gets up and sucks himself purple while the rest of us stand around drinking a '66 Beychevelle-les-deux-Coquettes which has proved so susceptible to travel as to render our afternoons as wretched as any I can remember.

This evening, three sherpas renounced Christianity.

BASE CAMP TWO: DAY ONE

Here at last, but a bitter coming we had of it. Simpson finally agreed to remain behind, but I should have suspected his leer. I last saw it immediately prior to the collapse of Zugspitz Agglomerates. He received word last evening of favourable Nepalese tax laws which persuaded him to set up a holding company here, Simpson Finance (Himalayas) Ltd. The loss of Simpson himself would be nothing, were it not that his puppet board of directors consists of our best eight porters, who have signed on the dotted line in return for six tins of pemmican per annum and a free go on Simpson's abominable secretary Beryl.

We have, in consequence, had to jettison the previously-portable sauna, six gross of frozen grouse, ten sides of smoked salmon, two barrels of Glenlivet, Murchison's Lagonda, Hardwicke's cocktail cabinet, Pomfret's suede sofa, Wilkinson's rowing machine, Sibley's chandelier, and my Louis Quinze escritoire with the ormolu scroll-work.

We all feel absolutely naked. As Wilkinson put it so pithily on our arrival, 'If a plane flew over, or anything, they'd take us for a bunch of bloody filing clerks.'

To make matters worse, we lost our hatstand in the Jumjee Glacier just before noon. I was all for sending a couple of sherpas down after it, until they all began jabbering some muck about the ghost of the fool who'd been carrying the thing.

BASE CAMP TWO: DAY THREE

Murchison very low. He has been mooning about these past two days while we waited for the fog to rise, and I had foolishly

128

attributed his low spirits to the loss of his Lagonda. Feeling, as expedition leader, that it fell to me to plumb what in anyone else would be his depths, I enquired of the fool this morning what was troubling him.

It transpired that, just before leaving England, Murchison had got his board to vote him £100 a day living-expenses, but only against receipts. Somehow, Murchison had got it into his head that the Mirabelle had a branch up here, or, at the very least, the Gavroche. There being nothing but fog, which is free, Murchison now feels himself to be several hundred pounds out of pocket, with no prospect whatever of the situation's improving.

I fear he will not be of this party long.

BASE CAMP THREE: DAY TWO

17,000 feet, and Murchison, of course, gone.

On arrival here yesterday, the man had the effrontery to request my endorsement of an expense bill which maintained that Murchison had paid out £847.30 in tips during the climb from Base Camp Two. Pressed, he replied that he had been assailed by mountain beggars who had padded away through the snow unnoticed by anyone else. Further pressed, he claimed that he had, in fact, given all his money to a Yeti to prevent its devouring the entire expedition. Held down by Wilkinson and Hardwicke, he shrieked that his wallet had been carried away in an avalanche, an Act of God specifically excluded from his all-risks policy.

None of this being true, we sent him back. I have no doubt whatever that Murchison will pass the next three months in Khatmandu, gorging himself to a standstill on yakburgers and haggling with restaurateurs over the premium on forged bills.

BASE CAMP FOUR: DAY THREE

I begin to feel the expedition jinxed. I write this with a heavy and an apprehensive heart.

For several days, Pomfret had been suffering terribly from lust. Not having brought his secretary along, in the hope that he might recruit a young and untouched Nepalese temp along our way (a hope which foundered), he had found the going increasingly difficult. Day by day, his eyes grew more hollow,

129

his face more haggard, his step more unsteady. Frequently, as we others would turn in for the night, poor Pomfret would mutter in his lonely sleeping-bag about his becoming a burden to the rest of the party, with his constant pestering of assistants not his own.

We attempted constantly to reassure him and raise his spirits, but to no avail.

A little after two o'clock yesterday, at the height of the blizzard, Pomfret said to me, in a pitiful croak:

'Miss Belwether and I are just going outside. We may be some time.'

Preoccupied with my charts, I paid the poor fellow little heed, and merely nodded absently.

When the blizzard cleared towards evening, the pair were discovered a little way from the camp, frozen solid.

He was a very gallant English gentleman.

The less said about that disloyal bitch of mine, however, the better.

NEAR BASE CAMP FIVE: DAY TWO
Murder breeds in my heart.

From where we huddle in our makeshift camp upon this narrow storm-blown ledge, Wilkinson and I can just see the fine sheltered sweep of Base Camp Five on its wide plateau, with beyond it the stunning panorama of the high Himalayas.

We can also see swines Hardwicke and Sibley pacing out floor-plans in the snow, watched by the nefarious ingrate I had taken to be just another porter, but who turned out, yesterday afternoon, to be none other than Sibley's architect, blacked up.

Already he has erected a billboard announcing commencement of work upon the Sibwicke Health Hydro, scheduled completion date June 1979. Mocked by his day-glo lettering, Wilkers and I crouch here, evicted!

Little did either of us realise when we arrived here yesterday morning that Hardwicke and Sibley owned the freehold on Base Camp Five, snapped up in Khatmandu for a pittance. Here it is that they plan to build a hermetically sealed leisure complex for the jaded executive palate, a thing to wipe the floor with alp and corniche, a greedy vision of fat farms and squash courts and heated pools; and illimitable profits, naturally, for

130

the vile traitors whom we have supported so long and so far. Even now, the rest of our sherpas are studying the arts of massage and room-service in the warmth of their inflatable staff-quarters!

The jumbo heliport is marked out in brandy bottles.

SOUTH COL: DAY ONE

Wilkinson and his secretary gone.

Upon arrival at the crevice below the overhang, of which I had such high hopes concerning myself and Ackroyd's girl a few short weeks ago, I decided therefore to do the decent thing and offer it to Wilkers and Hermione. Who would have realised the effect of their sudden body-warmth upon the sheer slabs of ancient snow?

I shall carry to my own grave the last sight of them whirling down into the terrible void, standing out from the white landslide like a single, giant, eight-pointed, pale pink snowflake.

THE SUMMIT

The blackest day of my life, though not entirely unanticipated: this has been a doomed quest. Just before noon, heart pounding, I dragged myself over the final rim. I stood erect. I unrolled my Union Jack. And then, emotion having fogged my goggles, I whipped them off, the better to place my flag.

I found myself looking at a small brass plaque testifying to the fact that the Sattu had been scaled a month before by eighty-seven directors of the Satsubishi Electronics Corporation.

So there will be no knighthood, now.

Like a Tea-tray in the Sky

ACCREDITED (AND DISCREDITED) Fleet Street practice it may be, but it is nevertheless deeply unsettling to return from one's holiday to find another bloke holding down one's job.

I do not, of course, refer to the mundane business of propping the bones in front of an Olivetti and tapping out tropes to swaddle tomorrow's hake and chips; I have not, as you can see, yet been dislodged from that small niche. No, what I am on about is that one day soon, Mr William Grut, bachelor in the parish of Sevenoaks, may well be orbiting the earth, chortling at his good fortune, while I stand bitter on the ground below, taking no part in his great enterprise beyond an envious upward scowl.

I single out Mr Grut only because he seems to me to be the likeliest starter from the short list of five Britons just selected to carry the Union Jack into the ebon void aboard the first Eurospace satellite, scheduled to ping off its pad in early 1980. I may be wrong: our first weightless hero may turn out to be Dr Rycroft, or Dr Ince, or Dr Mason, or even Mr Geoffrey Firman; all that can be said for certain this morning is that it will not be me.

Or, if you like, I. Personally, I have given up trying to make a grammatical impression on the world. Linguistic precision doesn't seem to have counted for much when Mr Gerald Kaufmann, Minister at the Department of Industry, was sifting through the mailbag of aspirants, so there is little chance that he will reconsider that sift at this late date and reinstate me in the running on the strength of adroit punctuation or ensuring that prepositions aren't something you end sentences with. Gerald, as will be shown later, had somewhat different priorities.

I must say that I had rather fancied my chances. Mooning in

holiday idleness over the past month, and knowing that, beyond the shimmering horizon, the D of I was flicking through the pile of applications, I caught myself time and again in fantasies of heroism I had not entertained for a quarter of a century, when, as I recall, I climbed the Skylon to rescue Margaret Lockwood and was awarded the Victoria Cross and a Claud Butler bicycle by a grateful nation.

For I had long resigned myself to practicalities, or, rather, impracticalities: should war come, very old subalterns will not be required to dash into No Man's Land, waving Webleys; the Test selectors, if they have not spotted my underarm lob by now, will certainly not call upon its services in the future, irrespective of what further depredations Kerry Packer wreaks in the current workforce; automatic transmission has allowed my heel-and-toe technique to wither to the point at which Niki Lauda may sleep soundly in his bed; I smoke too much for Everest, not to mention the fact that one uncircumspect morning cough would bring the whole lot sliding into Base Camp One; I do not like the sea, especially 25,000 miles of it, and, anyway, lone yachtsmen tend these days to outnumber haddock by something in the order of eight to one.

But space! Space requires nothing but the willingness to sit in it and whizz round! It is heroism by proxy, all the nuts and bolts are spannered on the ground at Houston, all the plots are plotted there, the knobs turned, the thinking thought. Astronauting is like riding on a leading rein: you pop a pill from time to time, you float about a bit, you take your pulse, you stare at the moon, you send messages to kings and in-laws, and when it's time to come down, they pick you up in a bucket and put your face on commemorative stamps.

It was the only heroic area left to me, and now it has gone to Grut. Always provided, mind, that he passes the further selection stage, since the whole business of putting a European in space closely resembles the Miss World Contest. I see that these five will join fifty-five other candidates from eleven European countries for selection by the European Space Agency, so Grut's chance is but a bare one in sixty. (Will he, I wonder, have to parade first in a dinner jacket, then in a space suit, finally in a lurex jockstrap and high white wedges, while Michael Aspel attempts to elicit from him the exact nature of the boutique he plans to open on his return to earth?)

But his chances are less important to me than his candidacy; for, with a little imagination on Kaufman's part, a little flexibility, a little unpredictability, it could so easily have been mine. But Gerald is nothing if not predictable, and his advisers are similarly tacky with his cautious trail: look at their five aspirant heroes, and you will see that they do not drink, they do not smoke, they engage in outdoor sports to the point of insatiability—Grut is the captain of the British free-fall parachute team (I trust the qualification will stand him in no stead whatever in the upcoming enterprise), Ince holds the Territorial Army trophy for canoeing from Devizes to Westminster (doubtless Kaufman spotted him from the Members' Terrace and calculated, astute judge of horseflesh that he is, that a bloke prepared to paddle from Wiltshire would happily go into space for little more than luncheon vouchers and a CBE), Mason is a glider pilot by hobby (and will, presumably, be ready to come down anywhere without complaining), while Mr Firmin spent two years in the Antarctic, which he has compared with outer space, though not to my satisfaction. They all play squash and cricket; two play tennis.

They are, in short, very old-fashioned British heroes, sporty, unaddicted, thin, clean-living, and possessed of that masochistic keenness which persuades men to jump off high things or crouch in sub-zero solitude for no other reason than that they are there.

How very trite of the Department! How very dated, how out of touch in a world where the cold shower has rightly become an object of derision and the school hero joins his nostrils with a safety-pin! And what will it do for Britain, should one of the Famous Five be selected, to have as its representative in space an exemplar of Victorian moral rectitude, a prim clean stoic bleeping elliptically around a world from whose contemporary texture he has long been disqualified by his predilection for parachuting onto the South Pole with nothing to sustain him but a bottle of Tizer and *Scouting For Boys*?

When we could have had a mature man, pleasingly flawed by experience, slightly overweight, perhaps, but only through his recognition of life's good things, a man who could be monitored upon a million international screens with a bottle of Glenlivet in one fist and a box of Partagas floating in readiness beside the other; a man of the New Order, unparochial, capable of ordering prawns in thirty languages and quoting airline safety injunctions in twenty more, thus enabling him to communicate on equal terms with the leaders of the polyglot hordes over which he passed, a man with several Irish jokes at his fingertips and fascinating opinions on almost everything there is (they would sit rapt in Houston, as he outlined the flaws in CAP during the still watches of the night or reassessed the career of Judy Garland); a man with a unique eau-de-nil lightweight suit, and a mocking laugh, both of which would linger in the terrestrial memory as his shiny module vanished into the darkness over Leningrad and Guam; a man whose hair was thinning just a little, who screamed occasionally at an untoward lurch or clunk, who began to sing *Fascination* as the booze level sank below the bottom of the label, who asked Houston to remind his wife to get a man in to look at the dishwasher; in short, a *human* man, not perfect, perhaps, yet somehow. . . .

Yet somehow overlooked, is what. Unless, that is, the D of I should have a change of heart. Or any heart at all.

Varnishing Trick

The Arts Council advertised for a Press Officer, so I applied.

> 23 Tudor Street,
> London, EC4,
> Europe,
> The World,
> The Solar System,
> Er, Space.

DEAR SIR,

I write to apply for the job of Press & Public Relations Officer. I hope you like the way I did the address just now. It's a whole new way of doing addresses, it has humour, it has information compactly presented, it really, you know, catches the eye. I deliberately left off the date; I think that's a pretty exciting thing to do, it involves the reader right away, he has to look at his watch, or if he doesn't have one of those date things, he has to go out and ask somebody what the date is, they perhaps have to look for a calendar together, it's sort of community art, it could be very big, I know it's something we in the British culture dynamic ought to associate ourselves with, we do not want to fall behind the Japs and similar in Low-Author-Profile Literature.

I just noticed I left out England between London EC4 and Europe. That wasn't deliberate, but I think I'll leave it anyway. it's sort of Negative Serendipity, wouldn't you say? I am of the opinion that error is a valid literary technique; I think we are all too hanged up on inaccuracy these days, it has taken a lot of the joy out of creation. Us Press & Public Relations Artists of the avant garde feel deeply about this.

136

You see that Er in front of Space, I take it? That connotes a concept midway between certainty and uncertainty, it's a whole new ball game, it's all about an author coming clean with his audience and saying: Yes, I accept current thinking about the universe, I am equally at home in the Two Cultures, I am *du fait* with what is going on all over, but that doesn't mean I don't have reservations, there's a lot in Oriental philosophy which points to the fact that the world is actually on the back of a fish, and who am I to come right out and say that that is a load of crap? There is more things in Heaven and Earth, Horace, know what I mean?

I'm not calling *you* Horace, of course. It's a quote, an echo, it's paying homage to the great tradition. We at the Arts Council, all right, *you* at the Arts Council at the present moment in time, must not be slaves to novelty at the expense of the great stuff which has gone before, such as Milton and similar, they had their moments, too, despite their oldness. I'm using Horace figuratively, I don't know your name, I suppose I could of looked it up, but I am not into research right now, research has killed more poetry than almost anything. As Marty Wilde said, I have my opinions, do not confuse me with the man on the Clapham omnibus.

Sleek, green, greasy, the gamma globulin of the pseudo-psyche pseeps through my psoriatic psoul. That was the day we all went to see *Gamma Globulin's Needle* at the Islington Theatre-In-The-Bus and it snowed and my father cried, and we came back home and roasted chestnuts in the fire, how they cracked and spluttered! *Wer reitet so spät durch Nacht und Wind?*

That's one of my portable paragraphs. You can cut it out and stick it anywhere in this letter, or, indeed, anywhere else, it will take on whole different resonances. I plan to do the same with my press releases, it could revolutionise the information business.

By the way, in case I didn't say so before, I am also very musical. I play the shower. In fact, I have written an entire symphony for bathroom fittings, including soap.

But how, I hear you saying, are we going to put across the right image of the Arts Council to the running lickspittles of the capitalist press conspiracy? It's a question which has occupied all of us in the Alternative Underground Advertising Business for some time now, viz., how do you get maximum national coverage for your plans to overthrow the fascist Fleet Street clique and replace them with the People's representatives, now that the moment has come for company cars and Mirabelle accounts to get spread around on a properly egalitarian basis?

Direct action is my way. I am heavily into non-verbal communication, and I think we could well use Arts Council funds to, say, seal off Fleet Street with barbed wire barricades and turn it over to one big auditorium where members of my staff could come on painted purple and mime things like the decline of the West and the difficulty of marketing obscene embroidery. If we pile some old scaffolding in the middle of the road, I am sure we could get the Tate to kick in with a grand or two, which would also come in handy when buying editors.

Can you tell from the enclosed photograph that I am nearly one-eighth Polish? There could also be Celtic somewhere in there, too, but Black I couldn't swear to, though I can do that clicking at the back of my throat and I once lived with two Matabele hookers who were doing it to subsidise a book about four-dimensional furniture they nearly sold to The Carcinoma Press. What I'm driving at is, I have rapports with all cultures, you name it. You want to mount an exhibition about Bulgarian topiary, you want to do a laser show on lesbian ovenware, you want to parachute singing sculptors into Pitlochry, I'll be right in there empathising.

I shall hold press conferences. The Arts Council never holds press conferences, that's why we, you, have such a lousy image, we could do things from airships, we could fly journalists to Djerba to launch our new range of anti-novels, we could get food correspondents to test edible paintings and throw in a cabaret gratis, I have seen Roy Strong's Jimmy Cagney and it's really terrific, you'd swear it was Humphrey Bogart, there's nothing we couldn't do. We have the money. And, speaking for myself, I have no objection to delivering press handouts in the nude, providing it's tastefully lit and emerges naturally from the script, I think there is nothing shameful about the human body, although I think you ought to know I will never engage in simulated acts in front of journalists or anybody else, until the pay improves.

As a matter of fact, hey, this has just occurred to me in a, like, flash, and isn't that the best way, who needs to consider, we could all be dead by the time we got around to conclusions, as a matter of fact, could we not consider Public Relations *itself* as a great art form, it would be entirely, what's the word, consonant with Arts Council policy of pushing aesthetic frontiers ever further until they could be anywhere? After all, now you really look at it, isn't the Arts Council just one big piece of PR shlock, just between you and I, isn't it the whole cosmetic bit, the Government's nose-job on its own philistinism, Anglo-Dummy Culture's silicone tit?

Not, of course, that, if chosen, I would ever come right out and say it. I mean, it's not my job.

The Rime of the Ancient Film-maker

There has been much speculation as to why, when Ken Russell's first film on the Lake Poets was so uncharacteristically restrained, his second was so characteristically extravagant.

Part I

An ancient director meeteth three viewers about to watch *Match of the Day*, and detaineth one.

It is an ancient Film-maker,
And he stoppeth one of three.
'By thy long grey script and glittering
                                      lens,
Now wherefore stopp'st thou me?

The telly's doors are open'd wide,
We've got the Guinness in;
There's cheese'n'bacon Krunchimunch,
And peanuts by the tin!'

He holds him with his podgy hand,
'There was a film,' quoth he.
'Eff off! It's Stoke v. QPR!'
Retort the Viewers three.

The viewer is spellbound by the old man's Arriflex. There may be money in it.

He holds one with his glittering lens—
The Viewer stood stock still:
'Is this for *Candid Camera?*'
The film-man hath his will.

The Viewer sat down on the step:
This could be fame at last!
And thus spake on that ancient man,
The mad-eyed cinéaste.

140

Mr Melvyn Bragg is hired, and works for an entire morning. The book is finished.

'The script was cheer'd, the treatment
                                        clear'd.
Granada coughed up loot!
I grabbed my crew and off we blew,
Bound for the first day's shoot.

The Sun came up upon the left,
Into the lens shone he!
A blood-red smear, a crimson tear,
Was all the lens could see!

The film-maker gets to the heart of Wordsworth.

'Cut! Print!' I cried; for in that shot
Was all I asked, and more:
A sense of doom, in that one zoom;
All Nature steep'd in gore!

Lake poetry is pain and lust
And death!' the old man roared.
'And—' here the Viewer turned his head,
For QPR had scored.

Warning to his theme, he hires six helicopters and an abattoir.

'And then—' the Viewer's head jerked
                                        back
'—we cut across to France.
In every scene, the guillotine:
Well, why pass up the chance?

A sonnet is carefully interpreted.

The fat heads roll'd, and, green with
                                        mould,
The rotting torsos lay;
While, nude, the Eskdale Shepherd
                                        gasped
And rutted in the hay!'

The viewer is amaz'd by the sheer vision of the ancient director.

'Stone me! Is all *that* poetry?'
The Viewer cried. 'By heck!
I only know The Boy Stood On
The, wossname, Burning Deck!'

141

'You have to read *between* the lines!
Between the *words*, forsooth!
For what *I* read is what *I* know:
There is no other Truth!

Granada, hearing
rumours, despatch a
studio spy.
But fools'—and here his face grew black—
'Will ne'er let genius be:
A man was sent from Manchester;
His brief: to check on *me*!

Each day, he scribbl'd telegrams
Back to Granada's boss;
Each day, his calculator clicked.
His name was Albert Ross.

The spy, in a vision,
foresees ratings.
And when he saw what we had shot,
His flannel chops turn'd white!
'You call *this* family viewing, son?
You call *this* Sunday night?'

Thereafter, sat he with our crew;
Thereafter, every day,
They fawned to do his every whim,
For they had heard him say,

The spy takes control of
the project.
That if the film did not pass *him*,
If there was one more shot
He could not show his grandmother,
Then he would scrap the lot!

The ancient director is
sold for a mess of pottage,
plus overtime.
And they were men with mortgages,
And they were men with wives:
There was no room for genius
Within their little lives!

I stood apart, as in a dream,
And let them shoot at will;
They filmed each lousy skylark, shot
Each stinking daffodil!

142

Yet, while I stood, my brain did not:
It, fertile, laid a plan;
A perfect crime, to wait the time
The film was in the can!

The ancient director
draws his own
conclusions!

And, as it left for Manchester,
I left to cut my loss;
And, with a Props Department bow,
I shot that Albert Ross!

Part II

A free man, the ancient
film-maker launches into
*The Rime of the Ancient
Mariner*.

'The Sun now rose upon the right:
We went to film Part Two.
But when they scann'd the scene I'd
                                    plann'd,
Rank terror gripp'd the crew!

They look'd behind, to ease their mind,
But no fat fink did follow!
Nor any day, with bonus pay,
Came to the film crew's Hollo!

Sheer brilliance
overwhelms doubt yet
again.

They did not guess; nor did they press
For further explanation:
Since genius brooks no challenge, and
Technicians know their station.

But Friday came; it brought no cash.
Their nagging made me cross.
And like a fool, I blew my cool:
Confess'd I'd murder'd Ross!

The film crew are deeply
stricken by news of the
poor wretch's death.

They shriek'd! They swore! They tore
                                    their hair!
They fell down in their woe!
For all averr'd I'd kill'd the bird
That made the cash to flow!

And when, next morn, I found my teeth,
Arose, and quit my bed;
There came no sound from all around:
The camera crew had fled!

And yet, and yet: my actors stood,
Waiting in serried ranks;
Thank God, I thought, that actors are
As thick as two short planks!

They stared at me, made-up and dress'd,
With simple, empty eyes.
And what I saw when I stared back
Were blessings in disguise!

The ancient film-maker
recognises his own
supreme qualities.

Who needs a camera crew? I cried;
Who needs their bleating moan?
I took the kit, and shoulder'd it,
And went to film alone!

And oh, the reds! And oh, the greens!
And oh, the clever angles!
And, bless my wig, is that a twig,
Or something Coleridge dangles?

The ancient film-maker
pre-empts critical
acclaim, wisely.

Was ever documentary made
So bravely to defy sense?
Is, surely, this not what is meant
By sheer poetic license?

For am I not a poet, too,
Indeed, not far less boring
Than all those Lakeland buggers—' he
Broke off. The man was snoring.

He jabbed his ribs; the Viewer woke.
'Who won?' he cried, 'Did Rangers?
I know Stoke's bleeding midfield play,
It's full of hidden dangers.'

144

The ancient film-maker
still struggles to
communicate, with no
more than usual success.

The ancient film-man grasped his throat!
'I talk of Art!' he cried;
'Of Culture for the masses!' 'Stoke's
A bloody tricky side,'

The Viewer said, 'they're all up front,
I've mentioned it before.'
A sadder (but no wiser) man,
He went to find the score.

Great Solved Unmurders of our Time

'*According to the Home Office publication,* Criminal Statistics, England and Wales, 1977, *murder is in decline. The number of homicides last year was the lowest for four years.*'—The Times

THE BRIGHT YALE KEY slipped three times, bouncing off the escutcheon-plate, scoring the lilac Dulux.

The fingers of Dr Kevin Clyde Crippen were very nervous. He dried finger and thumb on his lapel, tremblingly, and tried the lock again. This time, the key slid in, the lock turned, the front door of 39, Hilldrop Crescent, opened. He put a handkerchief to his face, and stepped quickly inside.

The smell of gas was very strong.

If it was this strong downstairs, he reasoned, then upstairs it would be more than adequate.

So he went upstairs, as the hall clock struck six am. He had last passed it at midnight, going out, Belle snoring ginnily on their bed, their unlit gas-fire hissing cheerlessly on the wall.

On the landing, he listened at the shut bedroom door. The hiss hissed on, but there was no other sound. He pulled the bath-towel out from beneath the door, and, heart hammering, turned the handle.

Belle Crippen lay motionless in the dawn light. A fearful little grin rippled her husband's Zapata moustache. He ran lightly downstairs again, two at a time, and plucked the phone from its cradle.

'Police? Oh my God, there's been a terrible accident, my darling wife is . . . '

'Silly little sod,' said Belle Crippen, 'leaving the gas on!'

146

She leaned across the kitchen table with two cups for the ambulancemen, allowing her peignoir to gape tantalisingly.

'Still,' she said, straightening up so that she brushed the standing constable, 'what can you expect? Bleeding useless at everything, catch my drift?'

The constable returned her wink. Come Tuesday, he was on early turn. Park the Panda round the back, couple of squirts of Brut from the glove compartment, good morning, Madam, pursuant to our enquiries concerning your fortunate escape last week . . .

'Your good lady was very lucky indeed, sir,' he said to Crippen, who was staring bitterly out of the kitchen window. 'Mind you, I'm very surprised you panicked, you being a medical man and everything. Didn't you know North Sea gas was non-toxic?'

'*Him?*' snorted Belle. 'Him *medical?* He's a philosopher. Or,' she added nastily, 'was. Soon after we was married, he jacked it in.'

'I couldn't think of anything to think about,' muttered Crippen, mainly to the cat. The cat took a chunk out of his ankle, and slunk away.

'He travels in sundries, now,' said Belle. 'Mainly Brillo and shoe-trees. Still,' she raised a plucked and pencilled eyebrow at the beefier of the two ambulancemen, 'it keeps him out of the house.'

'Yes,' said the constable loudly, eager to re-establish himself over the beefy ambulanceman, 'yes, your North Sea gas is completely non-poisonous . . . '

Crippen turned savagely on his heel, walked out of the kitchen, ran upstairs, sat on his bed, snatched a cigarette from his pack, and blew all the windows out. On his dazed head, his hairpiece smouldered to ash. His contact lenses had vaporised. Fillings rolled around on the floor of his mouth.

'. . . 'Course,' said the policeman, glancing up at the flaking ceiling, 'that is not to say it don't remain highly volatile.'

'Paraquat?' said the chemist. 'You must be joking!'

'It would be Vietnam all over again,' said his assistant. She wore a white tee-shirt with SAVE THE SHARK stencilled across her bra-less bust. 'For every defoliated twig,' she murmured, and her eyes filled with tears, 'a woodlouse dies.'

'I've got these weeds,' said Crippen apologetically.

'A weed is God's creature, too,' said the assistant. 'Ask yourself, do we have the right?'

'How about a pair of new sunglasses?' suggested the chemist. 'Just come in. Made in Stuttgart. They change colour with your mood. Or an electric nail-file, runs on solar batteries, wonderful for touring holidays, no wires, plugs, nothing.'

'Kalathane, perhaps?' pressed Crippen. 'My roses are covered in blackfly, I must . . .'

'It is their natural home,' said the assistant.

'Anyway, it's on our list,' said the chemist. 'Anything deadlier than TCP, you got to have a chit signed by a Chief Superintendent.'

'Well, what do you do if you have rats?' cried Crippen.

'You talk to them,' said the assistant. 'We must love one another, or die.'

'I know,' muttered Crippen, 'I know, I know.'

'Bloody hell!' exclaimed Jas. Rumbelow, Builder & Decorator, No Job Too Large Or Small. 'Stone me! Stroll on! Bloody hell!'

He gazed through the gaping hole in Crippen's dining-room ceiling, and gazed down again at the length of shattered joist by his feet.

'Is it bad?' enquired Crippen.

'*Is it bad?*' cried Jas. Rumbelow. 'He only asked me if it was bad, Adrian!'

'*Is it bad?*' cried Jas. Rumbelow's partner. 'Bloody hell! Stone me! Stroll on!'

'We've only just finished doing your bedroom, squire,' said Jas. Rumbelow. 'This'll most likely set you back another three hundred.'

'Plus materials,' said Adrian.

'Plus VAT,' said Jas. Rumbelow.

'What happened to it?' enquired Crippen.

'It's one of your High Alumina Cement joists,' replied Jas Rumbelow, stabbing at his pocket calculator.

'HAC,' said Adrian.

148

'These new bloody town houses,' said Jas. Rumbelow.

'I wouldn't give you a thank you for them,' said Adrian.

'I wouldn't live in one rent-free,' said his partner.

'What was you trying to do?' asked Adrian.

'I was trying to screw a hook in,' sighed Crippen. 'I was trying to hang a rope up.'

'Five hundred pounds?' shrieked Belle Crippen, when he told her about the dining-room. 'Well, that's our little trip to fashionable Benidorm up the spout then, isn't it? That is the kybosh on our scented nights down the El Fantastic beach disco! Goodbye souvenir genuine flamenco dancer table-lamps, goodbye outings to fascinating glass-blowers, goodbye . . . '

'Goodbye bloody dago deckchair attendants, is what you mean,' muttered Crippen, 'goodbye swarthy bleeding waiters, goodbye Spanish binmen, for all I know!'

'I'm sure I don't know to what you are referring,' said Belle, patting her coiffe. 'Is it my fault that men's passions are so easily inflamed? Not, of course, in all cases. Anyhow, I do not intend to deprive myself of a well-earned holiday on your account, Kevin, I shall probably be touring South Wales this year.'

'Oh, really?'

'By ambulance.'

He was standing at the sink. A carving-knife lay on the draining board. Somewhere in his temple, a small vein burst. His eyes misted. He snatched up the carving-knife.

As he spun round, he inadvertently banged it against the fridge.

The blade sheared off at the handle.

'Now look what you've done!' shrieked Belle. 'That was a present from Heron Books! I had to wade through the whole of bloody Trollope to get that—'

Crippen bent down slowly and picked up the blade.

Engraved along its flimsy side was: *Made in South Korea.*

'I'd like two one-way tickets to New York, please,' said

Crippen.

'Wouldn't we all?' replied the travel-agent. 'This time of year, you'd be lucky to get an Awayday to Clacton. Wouldn't settle for a caravan fortnight in Rochdale, would you, provide your own sheets?'

'No, thank you,' said Crippen.

'Next please,' said the travel-agent.

Dr Crippen stared gloomily at Tracy Le Neve across his kitchen table.

'I couldn't get the tickets,' he said.

'Oh, well,' she said.

'Do you still love me?' he said.

'I think we're into an ongoing relationship situation, if that's what you mean,' said Tracy.

'More or less,' muttered Crippen.

'I mean, love is a very, you know, bourgeois concept, right? It has all these bad vibes about possession. It's, like, emotional colonialism, right? Practically fascist.'

A key turned in the lock.

'Oh God!' cried Crippen. 'She's supposed to be at the hairdresser!'

'Cool it,' said Tracy. 'Hi! You have to be Belle, right?'

'And who, exactly, is this?' snapped Mrs Crippen.

'She's Miss Le Neve,' stuttered Crippen.

'Kevin and I have this thing going,' said Tracy pleasantly.

'Oh Jesus!' moaned Crippen.

'Pull this one,' said Belle.

'Yeah, I know,' said Tracy. 'The thing is, I'm very into sociology right now. I'm doing this paper on unlikely relationships and their interface with middle-class mores. He's kind of my, you know, project.'

'I wish you luck!' cried Belle, and laughed.

Tracy Le Neve laughed, too.

'But what I'm *really* into,' she said, 'is female consciousness-raising. I mean, sexual division is really very old hat, right? I think we have to experiment with a whole new desire-spectrum. I plan to go into that next. I may do my master's on it.' She paused. 'You know something, Belle? You're really a terrifically attractive person.'

'Ooooh!' simpered Mrs Crippen. 'Really?'

'Definitely,' said Tracy.

Crippen pushed his chair back, and walked out slowly into the hall, but nobody noticed.

He sat in the snug of the Rat & Cockle, drinking his fourth shandy.

'Mind if I join you?'

Crippen looked up. The other man had his collar under one ear, a black eye, and a split lip. Dried blood caked his nostrils. Not a pleasant sight, but the unaccustomed shandy had lulled Crippen's inhibitions.

'Not at all,' he said. 'What's happened to you, pardon my curiosity?'

The man sighed, sipped his Tuborg.

'I've been down Whitechapel, haven't I?' he replied. 'There was this big blonde leaning up against the wall, split skirt, fishnet tights, stiletto heels, enormous—' he glanced down at his hands. They were large, and shaking. 'I don't know what came over me, I sort of lost control, it appals me the way these women ply their revolting trade in the streets of our wonderful city, follow me, so I grabbed hold of her and . . . '

'Yes?' whispered Crippen.

'Turned out he was in the Parachute Regiment,' said the Ripper.

Gilded Cage

THE WATERY DAWN came up, to little interest. A cassowary honked, half-heartedly; Moskisson's potto squeaked, once; an elderly scorpion broke wind.

They had seen dawns before. There was no point kicking up an atavistic fuss. For one thing, you didn't have to scare breakfast into submission. It came on tin plates.

The lion yawned. Bound to be horse again. Nothing wrong with horse, mind, nice piece of shoulder, can't complain. Slides down a treat, horse.

The only thing was, you couldn't chase a chop. That was the whole trouble with convenience foods. You couldn't bring them down, play with them, scare the life out of them. Be nice, thought the lion wistfully, to hear your breakfast scream a bit, now and again.

He strolled to the bars, looked out.

'Hallo,' he said. 'Here's a do.'

His lioness turned over slowly on her hygienic concrete shelf. Her tail flopped down. She let it swing, idly. Cleaner up here than a tree, she thought, more modern, chamfered for easy maintenance, no moss, insects. And yet.

'What is it?' she said.

'They've duffed up another chimpanzee,' said her mate.

The lioness opened one eye. In the cage across the way, a chimpanzee lay on its back, hands, feet, teeth all clenched in an unmistakable rigor.

'Oh, that,' she murmured. She shut the eye again. 'New frail old chimp horror, anthropoid granny another victim of senseless violence, where will it end, see fabulous free knickers offer page nine.'

'You know who I blame?' said the lion. 'I blame the parents.'

The lioness snored.

152

At eight o'clock, two keepers came with a black polythene sack and removed the battered corpse.

The lion watched.

The tiger next door came to the front of its cage.

'Keepers won't even bother finding out who did it,' said the tiger. 'Right?'

'What's the point?' said the lion.

'What's the point?'

'Only let 'em off with a bloody caution,' said the lion.

'If that,' said the tiger.

'They'll blame it all on the environment,' said the lion gloomily. 'Am I right?'

'No question,' said the tiger.

'Impersonal high-rise steel cages, parents out picking one another's fleas off all day, lack of properly supervised play areas, catch my drift?'

'Absolutely,' said the tiger. 'Not to mention a cry for help.'

'I'd give 'em bleeding cry for help!' snapped the lion. 'When I was a cub, they'd have got the chop.

He drew a burnished claw across his throat, as only lions can.

'Bloody good job, too,' said the tiger.

'No messing about,' said the lion, 'eye for an eye, know what I mean?'

'Those were the days,' said the tiger.

At 11.30 am, the lioness jumped down from her shelf.

A keeper let her four cubs in.

She played with them for half an hour.

Then the keeper came and took them out again.

She jumped back up on her shelf, and began to groom.

'I don't call that motherhood,' said the lion.

The lioness shrugged. She rolled on her back, and looked at the ceiling of the cage.

'I ought to get a job,' she said. 'There's more to life than bringing up cubs.'

'You what?' cried the lion. 'A *lioness*? Getting a *job*?'

'While we're at it,' said his mate, 'I think I'll drop the ess. It is discriminatory; it is degrading. Lion, is what I am.'

The lion's claws sprang from their soft sheaths, instinctively.

'What kind of job?' he growled.

'Oh, I dunno,' she said. 'I could roar. I could terrorise visitors. I could attack the keeper.'

'*I* DO THAT!' thundered the lion, with such force that, on the other side of the Zoo, a small herd of antelope woke up, trembled violently, and ran into the wall. 'Any roaring, any terrorising, is down to *me*!'

'I could be just as good,' said the lioness.

'Oh yes! Ha, ha! Oh yes!' muttered the lion. He paced up and down furiously. 'Ha, ha! Oh yes! Very droll. Ha, ha!'

He hurled himself at the bars, and bit them.

'She'll be growing a mane next,' said the tiger next door.

'I blame the Zoo,' said the lion. 'The Zoo does everything for 'em, these days. Food, housing, education, all laid on, know what I mean, whatever happened to self-sufficiency, independence, responsibility?'

'You've been talking to Rhodes Bison,' said the tiger.

'Why not?' said the lion.

'Look at them dingoes,' said the lion, an hour or two later. 'They're at it like knives!'

'When I was young,' said the tiger, 'there was such a thing as courtship.'

'The magic's gone,' muttered the lion. 'I blame the Zoo. No restrictions any more. They used to move in and stop all that. They used to keep 'em apart, except for breeding seasons.'

'Permissiveness,' grunted the tiger.

'Comes back to what I was saying,' said the lion firmly. 'Too much time on their hands, too much done for 'em. In the old days, before the Zoo stepped in and took over everything, they never had no time for all that. Out foraging for food, fighting off enemies, building your own home, competing to survive—it bred a different class, built character, follow me?'

'You're talking about the jungle, now,' said the tiger, wistfully.

'Right!' cried the lion. 'Definitely!'

The dingoes shrieked to an umpteenth climax.

'They're like bloody animals,' muttered the lion.

The sparrow zipped through the bars, and landed on the edge of the lion's trough.

'I've just been up the Bird House,' it chirped. 'You wouldn't bloody credit it!'

'What?' said the lion.

'They just took delivery of two gross chrome bells, anodised ladders, mirrors, prefabricated nesting-boxes, you name it.'

'Oh, very nice!' said the lion sarcastically. 'I wonder how much that little lot set the Zoo back?'

'Birds,' twittered the sparrow, 'used to make their own entertainment. There's no end of things you can do with a good pebble, couple of bottle tops, fag-packets, all that. Now they just sit around waiting for the Zoo to provide everything, have you noticed?'

'Have *I* noticed?' cried the lion.

'Has *he* noticed?' said the tiger.

'They'll have Zoo-subsidised tellies next,' said the lion.

'He's not joking,' said the tiger.

The white Range Rover of the Zoo Vet Service rolled past. They watched it turn the bend.

'Elephant,' explained the sparrow. 'Got a bit of colic. I was just round there.'

'*Bit of colic?*' exclaimed the lion. 'Bloody stroll on! What would he do up India?'

'Wouldn't bother about it,' said the tiger, 'would he? More important things to think about. Knocking down trees, leading herds, working out how to get to the graveyard.'

'Stepping on tigers,' said the sparrow.

'Why not?' retorted the tiger. 'Part of life's rich texture. *And* if he did, would I go running to the doctor's? Would I buggery, I'd have a bit of a lick, pull myself together, get on with things, right?'

'You'd probably nip down the village and knock a couple of tribesmen back,' said the lion dreamily. He ran his purple tongue over his muzzle. 'Set you up a treat, that.'

'Better than free bloody medical treatment, anyway,' said the tiger.

'You know what bothers me more than anything?' said the lion, after a moment or two.

'What's that?' enquired the sparrow.

'It's like this,' said the lion. 'All our offspring are growing up in this mollycoddling bloody environment, right? Everything done for 'em, nothing demanded of 'em, all they got to do if they want anything is ask the Zoo, they get a handout, okay?'

'Get on with it,' muttered the tiger.

'What I'm saying is,' said the lion, 'what I'm saying *is*, what happens if the Zoo runs out of money? Overspends on services or whatever, and the whole operation starts falling to bits, health service breaks down, cages crumble, keepers pack it in, food gets short, amenities fold up. So there's all the bars fallen off, and there's all these animals wandering about with no-one to look after 'em or tell 'em what to do next, and because they've all grown up in the Zoo, would they have any idea of how to fend for themselves?'

'He's a bit of a thinker, this one,' said the sparrow.

'It'd all come back to them, wouldn't it?' said the tiger. 'I mean, it's in the blood. It's *natural*, right?'

The lion shrugged. He looked at his paw, wondering what it would be like to feel grass under it.

'It's only a thought,' he said.

A Little Touch of Harry in the Night

EYES UNGUM, and shards of dream whizz off into the corners of the dark.

It is three am exactly. We have the most luminous bedside clock in the world. You could read an insurance policy by it. It even has a luminous sweep second hand like a tiny radar screen. On bad nights, I sometimes fancy alien blips appear upon it, homing in from some far steppe to blat my premises. God knows how much radioactivity the thing is pumping out; every day, I examine the kids for the first tell-tale indications of genetic interference, an extra toe, perhaps, the bud of a new ear.

If the SALT talks ever succeed, clocks like mine will have to be turned in at local nicks.

Summer heat it was that woke me. I am wet. The arm upon the duvet gleams back the phosphorescence like a large sardine. Strange thing, the duvet: how were the world's ducks so ready for its boom? A sudden need for a billion billion feathers; and it was met.

Where did they find the men to pluck them? Can it be possible, I ask myself at 3.02 with all the libraries shut, that ducks can be plucked automatically, that there are huge machines with adroit tin fingers capable of stripping a duck in milliseconds?

Probably not. I have heard, I recall by 3.04, that the bulk of the world's duckdown comes from China; with ten thousand million digits on tap, an unprecedented hunger for feathers can doubtless be met with ease. Perhaps duckpluckers moonlight, out there beneath the rising sun; go off to the paddy fields of a morning with a bag of dead ducks round their necks, make an extra bob or two between rice-pickings. Possibly—they are fly, Orientals—they have developed a spry cyclic rhythm, enabling them to pluck and pick in syncopation, a duck under each arm

157

like a tiny bagpipe, while the thoughts of Chairman Hua tannoy across the echoing plain.

But.

It is 3.06.

But what about all those plucked bodies? Why, with the duvet boom, has the price of duckmeat not fallen to rock bottom, dipped below scrag and coley? Why do the kids not queue at chippies for ten pennorth of duck and a bag of beaks for the cat?

Can it be that the meat remains in China while the feathers fly westwards, that the happy Chinese nightly dine on crispy Pekin duck, cunning proof from Chairman Hua that the dark days of the Gang of Four are gone, that China is moving into the broad sunny uplands, next year everybody gets a Fiat 127, a Sony sound-system, an Austin Reed smock? Could this be behind the mollifying murmurs issuing towards Washington of late? Is their intensifying hatred of Sovietism bred from this new taste of the good life, duckstains on the bib and feather-money in the wallet?

A thought to sleep on, if I could. Nor shall I ever, unless these columns of marching ducks can be erased from the imagination. Beside the clock stands a radio; it came with one of those little plastic plugs on a string. STICK THIS IN YOUR EAR FOR INDIVIDUAL LISTENING AT ABSOLUTELY NO EXTRA COST. I have never stuck it in my ear before, partly because I did not wish to walk around and have sympathetic people bending down to shout in my radio, partly because mine has never been a name to conjure with in ear-nose-and-throat circles, and I have no idea what happens in those Eustachian depths after you get past the dusty bit. I know only that it's connected up by tunnels inside the head, and have always, therefore, lived in terror of shoving something in my ear and finding it stuck in my nose. Especially a radio.

Still, it is 3.14, a time at which normal strictures tend to waive themselves. I poke, gingerly, the little cone in my ear, pop the other end in the trannie, switch on. Tinny sounds resonate in all the bones of my head, crotchets plunk among my fillings. I thumb the tuner, find an English voice: it is some appalling phone-in freak, apparently blaming the loss of his wife's libido on illegal immigrants. Soporific enough stuff, the ducks fade, the eyelids leaden, and then some cheery swine in the studio informs the freak that we are taking a break there and will be back after the 3.15 news, and another cheery swine announces that he is in the newsroom and that they have just found the bowels of Henry V in a jamjar in Vincennes.

The eyes snap open again.

It occurs to me to wake my wife, despite the dangerous care I have just taken not to do so, either to corroborate what I think I have just heard or to get her to flick through the yellow pages for a 24-hour psychiatric service while I slip into something which will look natty under a strait-jacket.

I cannot. Fascination seems to have paralysed me. The newscaster is expatiating upon his ghastly headline, and I dare not miss a phrase. It turns out that Henry died of dysentery on an inconveniently hot August afternoon and the only way to get him from France to England for burial without considerable embarrassment was to put his insides in a pot, chop up his body, boil it in aromatics, then ship it to Westminster Abbey in a lead trunk.

End of news item, the cheery swine passes on to the Scotland–Iran result; I wait to hear whether there are any plans to put Ally MacLeod's giblets in a pot, chop up his body, boil it in McEwan's and ship it to Hampden Park in case anybody wants to do anything really nasty to it, but none is mooted, so I switch off and leave my ringing head alone with its insomniac thoughts.

They held life cheap, in 1422. In 1978, you can get six months for chucking a bottle at a Royal car, but I have little doubt that the repugnant mediaeval mortician who thought up the scheme to take a bandsaw to his monarch picked up a baronial gong for his ghastly initiative, leaving his modern descendants to glare out over their twelve million acres of Lincolnshire as they contemplate letters to the *Telegraph* urging the return of drawing and quartering for shop stewards.

It is 3.22.

I have great trouble shaking this image of Laurence Olivier with dotted lines all over him, like a butcher's chart. Of course, the real Harry was a lot shorter. Hardly a day goes by without someone telling me that mediaeval Britons were very short, because all the suits of armour we have are four feet tall. It never

159

seems to have occurred to anyone that it was only the soldiers who were short—every time a war came along, it is quite possible that the tall people went round to the short people and explained that it was time to go and fight for king and country if they didn't want their faces bashed in. Being short, they immediately complied. It doubtless made it easier on the industrial-military complexes of the day, too, whose interests have ever been served first: far simpler, far more cost-effective, to bang out ten thousand pairs of iron trousers with an eighteen-inch inside leg than having blokes coming back for second fittings with the Armada at the gate, could you hammer the crotch out a bit, and while you're at it how about brazing on a couple of patch pockets?

Of course, it being 3.25, it is quite possible that if the Carter–Brezhnev relationship gets any tackier and the Sino-American detente continues to improve, Britain will soon be in a position to flog its suits of armour to the Chinese and thus keep the Canaletto from going abroad. Just the right height, the Chinese, I can see them clanking out in serried ranks to face the Russians along the Ussuri River, pausing only to shove their visors up and poke a duck sandwich inside.

'ONCE MORE UNTO THE BLEACH, DEAR. . .'

Funny thing, history.

Tweak the continuum, put a tuck in a mezozoic fold, let the pterodactyl hang on for an eon or two, and it might well have been King Jimmy V extending his gauntlet beneath the fluttering pennants:

'Well met, proud Brooklyn! And good morrow, Bronx!
Dear Arizona, first of all my dukes!
How fares our brave Lord Twin Forks, and what news
Of Bishop Tombstone may we yet expect?
Comes Deadwood soon, and is. . .'

Not that any of it would make much difference, in the long run. Men would still pluck ducks, get dysentery, fight, be buried, and lie beside their wives in summer dawns, waiting for the sun to rise.